D1001493

The Kosta Boda Book Of Glass

This collection is current as of June 1, 1986.

I en tid när livet snurrar på allt hastigare, och produkter konsumeras och förbrukas lika snabbt som de producerats, finns det fortfarande något som skapas omsorgsfullt och långsamt.

Kosta Boda glas och kristall.

Här krävs det fortfarande ett arbetslag på 5 personer för att skapa ett vinglas.

Här vandrar formgivarna fortfarande genom hyttan, synar färgen på en vas, rundningen på en skål.

Och form-makarna snidar fortfarande sina formar, precis som de gjort sedan 1742.

I de små samhällena Kosta, Boda, Johansfors och Åfors finns det inte mycket som distraherar från glastillverkningen. Skogen står tät och tyst runt de fyra bruken.

Det var skogen som lockade hit de första glasmästarna för nära 250 år sedan. Den gav bränsle till ugnarna, virke till hus och hyttor.

Det första som producerades var fönsterglas, men snart blåstes vaser och skålar, glas och konstföremål. Pjäser som vi idag kan hitta på muséer och i samlingar över hela världen.

Allt är fött här, djupt i den Småländska skogen.

Det är här fantasi förvandlas till glas.

In an age of fast food, fast cars, and fast living, there is still something that is made slowly and carefully. The glass of Kosta Boda.

Here teams of five men still gather to make one wine glass. Artists still wander through the workrooms, picking up a vase here, a bowl there, checking the purity of color, the cleanness of an edge. And the mold maker still carves his precise shapes from a log he's just brushed the snow from.

In the small villages of Kosta, Boda, Johansfors and Åfors, there is little to distract one from the glass. Aside from the glassworks, a restaurant, and a few stores, there is nothing here but fir and birch trees. Forests that attracted the early glassmakers in the 1740s, when Kosta Boda began. They found everything they needed here to perfect their magic–wood, water, fire and solitude.

Originally, Kosta Boda made window glass. Soon, though, they were blowing crystal bowls, vases, stemware. The kind of pieces that can be found today in museums in London, the Cooper-Hewitt in New York, and the Royal Palace in Stockholm.

Yet each piece is born in the same place, deep in the woods of Sweden.

It is here that beautiful ideas are spun into molten glass.

LA COMPAGNIE

Alors que la restauration rapide, les voitures rapides et la vie rapide prédominent dans la période où nous vivons, on peut encore trouver des objets fabriqués lentement et soigneusement. C'est le verre de Kosta Boda.

Cinq hommes se réunissent encore en équipe pour fabriquer un verre à vin. Les artistes se promènent toujours dans les ateliers, examinant un vase ici, une coupe là pour en vérifier la pureté de la couleur et la netteté du bord. Le fabricant d'un moule taille toujours avec précaution des formes diverses dans un bûche dont il vient d'enlever la neige.

Dans les petits villages de Kosta, Boda, Johansfors et Åfors, il n'y a pas grand chose qui puisse distraire de l'attention portée au verre. En dehors de la fabrique de verre, d'un restaurant et de quelques magasins, on n'y trouve que des sapins et des bouleaux. Ce sont les forêts qui attirèrent les ouvriers-verriers aux alentours de 1742, au moment où a été fondé Kosta Boda. Ils y ont trouvé tout ce dont ils avaient besoin pour perfectionner leur pouvoir magique–le bois, l'eau, le feu et la solitude.

Au début Kosta Boda a fabriqué du verre à vitre. Très vite, toutefois, ils se mirent à souffler le verre pour fabriquer des coupes, des vases et des verres à pied en cristal. Aujourd'hui, on peut voir tous ces objets dans les musées de Londres, au Cooper Hewitt à New York et au Palais Royal de Stockholm.

Mais chaque pièce vient du même endroit, loin dans les forêts de Suède.

C'est là où les belles idées se profilent en verre coulé.

DIE FIRMA

In dieser Zeit von Schnellgerichten, schnellen Autos und schnellem Leben gibt es noch etwas, das langsam und sorgfältig hergestellt wird. Das Glas von Kosta Boda.

In der Zusammenarbeit von fünf Männern entsteht hier noch ein, einzelnes Weinglas. Die Künstler durchstreifen die Arbeitsräume, überprüfen die Echtheit der Farben und die Sauberkeit der Kanten von Vasen und Schalen. Der Schnee wird noch weggewischt von dem Klotz, den der Former in einen präzisen Umriss schnitzt.

In den kleinen Dörfern Kosta, Boda, Johansfors und Afors gibt es wenig Ablenkung von der Glasbläserei. Ausser den Glashütten, einem Restaurant und ein paar Geschäften sieht man nur Birken und Tannenbäume. 1742 der Anfang von Kosta Boda, wurden die ersten Glasbläser von diesen Wäldern angezogen. Sie fanden alles was sie brauchten, um ihren Zauber zu vollenden-, Holz, Wasser, Feuer und Abgeschiedenheit.

Kosta Boda war ursprünglich bekannt für die Herstellung von Fensterglas. Doch sehr bald wurden kristallene Schalen, Vasen und Stielgläser geblasen. Verschiedene Stücke können heute in Museen in London dem Cooper-Hewitt in New York und dem Royal Palast in Stockholm gefunden werden. Jedes Stück ist am selben Platz geboren, tief in den Wäldern von Schweden.

Hier werden wundervolle Ideen in geschmolzenes Glas geblasen.

Monica Backström: Född 1939 i Stockholm. Utställningar i Skandinavien, USA, Holland, England, Japan, Spanien och Tyskland. Representerad på Corning Museum i New York och muséer i Skandinavien.

Lisa Bauer: Född 1920. Utställningar i Sverige, Australien, Paris och Singapore. Representerad på flera skandinaviska muséer och på Corning Museum i New York.

Elis Bergh: (1881-1954). En av Kosta Bodas första formgivare i detta århundrade. Elis hade en varierad designkarriär; innan de 21 åren med Kosta Boda ritade han hus, lampor och smycken.

Bengt Edenfalk: Född 1924. Utställningar i Sverige, New York, Milano, Schweiz och Holland. Bengts verk är representerade på Nationalmuséet i Stockholm och Corning Museum i New York.

Anna Ehrner: Född 1948 i Stockholm. Utställningar i Stockholm, Köpenhamn, Tyskland och Japan. Annas arbeten är representerade på muséer i Stockholm och Göteborg.

Kjell Engman: Född 1946 i Stockholm. Utställningar i Sverige, Köpenhamn, Norge, Berlin och USA.

Paul Hoff: Född 1945 i Stockholm. Utställningar i Sverige, Europa, Japan, Australien och USA. Han finns representerad på Nationalmuséet i Stockholm och Corning Museum i New York, bland många andra.

Ulrika Hydman-Vallien: Född 1938 i Stockholm. Utställningar i New York, Tokyo, London, Paris, Tel Aviv och Stockholm. Representerad på bl.a. Victoria and Albert Museum i London, Corning Museum i New York, National Museum of Modern Art i Tokyo, samt Kung Gustav VI Adolfs Samling i Stockholm.

Gun Lindblad: Född 1954 i Lappland. Utställningar i Norge, Schweiz och Sverige.

Vicke Lindstrand: (1904-1983) Utställningar i Milano, Paris, New York och Sverige. Vickes offentliga arbeten bestod bl.a. av ett nära 7 meter högt glasfönster på Svenska Paviljongen i Paris och en glasfontän i New York.

Sigurd Persson: Född 1914. Utställningar i Sverige, London, New York, Tyskland och på Kuba. Representerad på muséer i Schweiz, Tyskland, England och USA.

Signe Persson-Melin: Född 1925. Utbildad på Konstfackskolan i Stockholm, Kunsthaandverkerskolen och Kunstakademien i Köpenhamn. Signes arbeten finns i flera offentliga lokaler i Sverige, till exempel Folkets Hus i Stockholm.

Rolf Sinnemark: Född 1941 i Stockholm. Utställningar i USA, Australien, Sverige och Danmark. Representerad bl.a. på Victoria and Albert Museum i London och Cooper-Hewitt Museum i New York.

Christian von Sydow: Född 1950. Utställningar i Sverige och Italien. Han finns representerad på flera svenska museer, bland annat Nationalmuséet i Stockholm.

Bertil Vallien: Född 1938 i Stockholm. Utställningar i New York, Los Angeles, Montreal, Sydney, Amsterdam, Danmark och Sverige. Han finns representerad på flera svenska muséer, Victoria and Albert Museum i London, Corning Museum i New York, samt i Kung Gustav VI Adolfs samlingar.

Ann Wärff: Född 1937 i Västtyskland. Utställningar i London, Paris, Stuttgart, Amsterdam, och på flera ställen i Skandinavien. Ann är representerad på Victoria and Albert Museum i London, Metropolitanmuséet i New York och Musée des Arts Decoratifs i Paris.

Göran Wärff: Född 1933 på Gotland. Utställningar i Sverige, Tyskland, Australien, Amsterdam, London, Paris, Tokyo, Toronto och New York.

THE DESIGNERS

Monica Backström: Born 1939, Stockholm. Exhibitions in Scandinavia, USA, Holland, England, Japan, Spain, Germany. Works represented in The Corning Museum, New York, and throughout Scandinavia.

Lisa Bauer: Born 1920. Exhibitions in Sweden, Australia, Paris, Singapore. Works currently in several Scandinavian museums, and the Corning Museum, New York.

Elis Bergh: (1881-1954) One of Kosta Boda's early designers of this century, he had a varied design career. Before his 21 years of work with Kosta Boda, he designed architecture, lamps and gold jewelry.

Bengt Edenfalk: Born 1924. Exhibitions in Sweden, New York, Milan, Switzerland, Holland. His work is represented in Nationalmuseum, Stockholm, and the Corning Museum in New York.

Anna Ehrner: Born 1948, Stockholm. Exhibitions in Stockholm, Denmark, Japan, Germany and Copenhagen. Her work is represented in museums in Stockholm and Gothenburg.

Kjell Engman: Born 1946, Stockholm. Exhibitions in Sweden, Copenhagen, Norway, Berlin and USA.

Paul Hoff: Born 1945, Stockholm. Exhibitions throughout Sweden, Europe, Japan, Australia and the United States. His work is represented in the Nationalmuseum in Stockholm, and New York's Corning Museum among others.

Ulrica Hydman-Vallien: Born 1938, Stockholm. Exhibitions in New York, Tokyo, London, Paris, Sydney, Tel Aviv, and Stockholm. Works represented in museums such as Victoria and Albert , London, Corning Museum, New York, National Museum of Modern Art, Tokyo and King Gustav VI Adolf's Collection, Stockholm.

Gun Lindblad: Born 1954, Lappland. Exhibitions in Norway, Finland, Switzerland, and Sweden.

Vicke Lindstrand: (1904-1983). Exhibitions include those in Milan, Paris, New York and Sweden. His public works have included a 22′ high glass window at the Swedish Pavillion in Paris and a glass fountain in New York.

Sigurd Persson: Born 1914. Exhibitions in Sweden, Cuba, London, New York and Germany. Works represented in museums in Switzerland, Germany, England and the USA.

Signe Persson-Melin: Born 1925. Attended the Swedish State School of Art and Design, and the Kunstakademien in Copenhagen. Work represented in several public sites throughout Sweden.

Rolf Sinnemark: Born 1941, Stockholm. Exhibitions in Colorado, Australia, Sweden, Denmark. His work is represented in Victoria and Albert Museum, London and the Cooper-Hewitt Museum, New York.

Christian von Sydow: Born 1950, Sweden. Exhibitions in Sweden and Italy. Works represented at several Swedish museums, including the Nationalmuseum in Stockholm.

Bertil Vallien: Born 1938, Stockholm. Exhibitions in Los Angeles, New York, Montreal, Sydney, Amsterdam, Denmark, and Sweden. His work is represented in several Swedish Museums, Victoria and Albert in London, Corning Museum in New York and King Gustav VI Adolf's Collection.

Ann Wärff: Born 1937, West Germany. Exhibitions in London, Paris, Stuttgart, Amsterdam, and throughout Scandinavia. Works represented in Victoria and Albert Museum, London, Metropolitan Museum of Art, New York and Musée des Arts Decoratifs, Paris, as well as many other collections.

Göran Wärff: Born 1933, Gotland. Exhibitions in Sweden, Australia, Amsterdam, London, Paris, Tokyo, Germany, Toronto, and New York.

LES DESIGNERS

Monica Backström: Née en 1939 à Stockholm. Expositions en Scandinavie, Hollande, Angleterre, Espagne, Allemagne, aux Etats-Unis et au Japon. Ses oeuvres figurent au Musée Corning dans l'Etat de New York et dans neuf musées scandinaves.

Lisa Bauer: Née en 1920. Expositions en Suède, Australie, à Paris et Singapour. Ses oeuvres se trouvent actuellement dans plusieurs musées scandinaves et au Musée Corning dans l'Etat de New York.

Elis Bergh: (1881-1954). L'un des premiers designers de ce siècle à Kosta Boda. Il a fait une carrière très variée. Avant les vingt et un ans qu'il a passés chez Kosta Boda, il a commencé par des dessins d'architecture, de lampes et de bijoux en or.

Bengt Edenfalk: Né en 1924. Expositions en Suède, Suisse, Hollande, à New York et Milan. Ses oeuvres figurent au Nationalmuseum de Stockholm et au Musée Corning dans l'Etat de New York.

Anna Ehrner: Née en 1948 à Stockholm. Expositions à Stockholm et Copenhague, au Danemark, Japon et en Allemagne. Ses oeuvres figurent dans les musées de Stockholm et de Göteborg.

Kjell Engman: Né en 1946 à Stockholm. Expositions en Suède, Norvège, aux Etats-Unis, à Copenhague et à Berlin.

Paul Hoff: Né en 1945 à Stockholm. Expositions en Suède, Europe, Australie, au Japon et aux Etats-Unis. Ses oeuvres figurent au Nationalmuseet à Stockholm et au Musée Corning dans l'Etat de New York.

Ulrika Hydman-Vallien: Née en 1938 à Stockholm. Expositions à New York, Tokyo, Londres, Paris, Sydney, Tel Aviv et Stockholm. Ses oeuvres figurent dans plusieurs musées comme le Victoria et Albert à Londres, le Musée Corning dans l'Etat de New York, le Musée National d'Art Moderne à Tokyo et la Collection du Roi Gustave VI Adolf à Stockholm.

Gun Lindblad: Née en 1954 en Laponie. Expositions en Norvège, Finlande, Suisse, et Suède.

Vicke Lindstrand: (1904-1983) Expositions à Milan, Paris, New York et en Suède. Parmi ses oeuvres de travaux publics existe une fenêtre de 6m,70 de haut au Pavillon de Suède à Paris et une fontaine de verre à New York.

Sigurd Persson: Né en 1914. Expositions en Suède, Allemagne, à Cuba, Londres et New York. Ses oeuvres figurent dans les musées de Suisse, d'Allemagne, d'Angleterre et des Etats-Unis.

Signe Persson-Melin: Née en 1925. Elle a fait ses études à la Swedish School of Art and Design et à la Kunstakademien de Copenhague. Ses oeuvres sont exposées dans différents lieux publiques en Suède.

Rolf Sinnemark: Né en 1941 à Stockholm. Expositions au Colorado, Danemark, Australie et en Suède. Ses oeuvres figurent au Musée Victoria et Albert à Londres, au Cooper-Hewitt dans l'Etat de New York et dans plusieurs musées suédois.

Christian von Sydow: Né en 1950 en Suède. Expositions en Suède et en Italie. Ses oeuvres figurent dans plusieurs musées de Suède, y compris le Nationalmuseum à Stockholm.

Bertil Vallien: Né en 1938 à Stockholm. Expositions à Los Angeles, New York, Montréal, Sydney, Amsterdam, au Danemark et en Suède. Ses oeuvres figurent dans plusieurs Musées de Suède, le Victoria et Albert de Londres, le Musée Corning dans l'Etat de New York et la Collection du Roi Gustave VI Adolf à Stockholm.

Ann Wärff: Née en 1937, Allemagne de l'ouest. Expositions à Londres, Paris, Stuttgart, Amsterdam et dans toute la Scandinavie. Ses oeuvres sont exposées au Victoria and Albert Museum à Londres, au Metropolitan Museum of Art à New York, au Musée des Arts Décoratifs à Paris, ainsi que dans de nombreuses autres collections en Europe et en Scandinavie.

Göran Wärff: Né en 1933 au Gotland. Expositions en Suède, Australie, Allemagne, à Amsterdam, Londres, Paris, Tokyo, et New York.

DIE ENTWERFER

Monica Backström: 1939 in Stockholm geboren. Ausstellungen in Skandinavien, Amerika, Holland, England, Japan, Spanien und Deutschland. Ihre Kunstwerke sind im Corning Museum in New York und verschiedenen Museen in Skandinavien zu besichtigen.

Lisa Bauer: 1920 geboren. Ausstellungen in Schweden, Australien, Paris, Singapur. Ihre Kunst ist in verschiedenen skandinavischen Museen und dem Corning Museum in New York zu besichtigen.

Elis Bergh: 1881-1954. Eine umfangreiche Karriere als Entwerfer und einer von Kosta Boda's ersten Entwerfern dieses Jahrhunderts. Er schaffte Entwürfe von Baukunst, Lampen und Goldschmuck, bevor er seine 21 jährige Laufbahn mit Kosta Boda antrat.

Bengt Edenfalk: 1924 geboren. Ausstellungen in Schweden, New York, Mailand, Schweiz und Holland. Seine Kunst ist im National Museum Stockholm und dem Corning Museum in New York zu besichtigen.

Anna Ehrner: 1948 in Stockholm geboren. Ausstellungen in Stockholm, Dänemark, Japan, Deutschland und Kopenhagen. Ihre Kunst ist in Museen in Stockholm und Göteborg zu besichtigen.

Kjell Engman: 1946 in Stockholm geboren. Ausstellungen in Schweden, Kopenhagen, Norwegen, Berlin, und Amerika.

Paul Hoff: 1945 in Stockholm geboren. Ausstellungen in Schweden, Europa, Japan, Australien und Amerika. Seine Kunstwerke sind im National Museum in Stockholm und im Corning Museum in New York zu besichtigen.

Ulrika Hydman-Vallien: 1938 in Stockholm geboren. Ausstellungen in New York, Tokyo, London, Paris, Sydney, Tel Aviv und Stockholm. Die Kunstwerke sind im Victoria und Albert Museum London, Corning Museum New York, Nationales Museum für moderne Kunst- Tokyo, König Gustav VI Adolfs' Sammlung in Stockholm.

Gun Lindblad: 1954 in Lappland geboren. Ausstellungen in Norwegen, Finnland, Schweiz und Schweden. Sie ist eine von Kosta Boda's jüngeren Entwerfern.

Vicke Lindstrand: 1904-1983. Ausstellungen in Mailand, Paris, New York und Schweden. Seine Kunstwerke umfassen ein 22″ hohes Glasfenster im schwedischen Pavillon in Paris und einen Glasspringbrunnen in New York.

Sigurd Persson: 1914 geboren. Ausstellungen in Schweden, Kuba, London, New York und Deutschland. Seine Kunstwerke sind in Museen in der Schweiz, Deutschland, England und der USA zu besichtigen.

Signe Persson-Melin: 1925 geboren. Besuchte die staatliche, schwedische Kunst- und Design Schule und die Kunstakademien in Kopenhagen. Ihre Arbeit ist representiert in verschiedenen öffentlichen Plätzen in Schweden.

Rolf Sinnemark: 1941 in Stockholm geboren. Ausstellungen in Colorado, Australien, Schweden und Dänemark. Seine Arbeit ist im Victoria und Albert Museum in London, dem Cooper-Hewitt Museum in New York und verschiedenen schwedischen Museen zu besichtigen.

Christian von Sydow: 1950 in Schweden geboren. Ausstellungen in Schweden und Italien. Seine Arbeit ist in verschiedenen schwedischen Museen und dem National Museum in Stockholm zu besichtigen.

Bertil Vallien: 1938 in Stockholm geboren. Ausstellungen in Los Angeles, New York, Montreal, Sydney, Amsterdam, Dänemark und Schweden. Seine Arbeit ist in verschiedenen schwedischen Museen, Victoria und Albert Museum in London, Corning Museum in New York und König Gustav VI Adolfs' Sammlung in Stockholm, zu besichtigen.

Ann Wärff: 1937 in West Deutschland geboren. Ausstellungen in London, Paris, Stuttgart, Amsterdam und Schweden. Ihre Arbeit ist representiert im Victoria und Albert Museum, London, Metropolitan Museum der Kunst, New York, Musee des Arts Decoratifs, Paris und vielen anderen Kollektionen.

Göran Wärff: 1933 in Gotland geboren. Ausstellungen in Schweden, Australien, Amsterdam, London, Paris, Tokyo, Deutschland, Toronto und New York.

The Index.

KOSTA BODA FÖRBEHÅLLER SIG RÄTTEN ATT GÖRA ÄNDRINGAR I KOLLEKTIONEN.
ALLA ANGIVNA MÅTT ÄR UNGEFÄRLIGA OCH KAN VARIERA NÅGOT EFTERSOM GLASET ÄR HANDGJORT.

KOSTA BODA RESERVES THE RIGHT TO MAKE ADJUSTMENTS IN THE COLLECTION.
PLEASE NOTE THAT ALL MEASUREMENTS GIVEN ARE APPROXIMATE DUE TO THE HAND-MADE NATURE OF THE GLASS.

KOSTA BODA SE RÉSERVE LE DROIT DE FAIRE DES CHANGEMENTS DANS LA COLLECTION.
NOUS VOUS DEMANDONS DE NOTER QUE TOUTES LES MESURES SONT APPROXIMATIVES CAR TOUT EST FABRIQUÉ À LA MAIN.

KOSTA BODA BESITZT DAS RECHT JEGLICHER NACHAHMUNG IN DER KOLLEKTION.
DURCH DIE HANDVERARBEITUNG DES GLASES IST JEGLICHE ABMESSUNG NUR ANNÄHERND.

Index by

Ashtrays. Askfat

Barware. Barserviser

Bowls. Skålar

Candleholders Ljusstakar

Decanters and Jugs Karaffer och kannor

Dishes. Fat

Ice Buckets, wine coolers Ishinkar, vinkylare

Lamps. Lampor

Miniatures. Miniatyrer

Function.

Paperweights and blocks Brevpressar och block

Stemware. Glasserviser

Vases. Vaser

Miscellaneous. Övrigt

Addresses Adresser

Index by

Stemware
Glasserviser

Vases. Vaser

Bowls. Skålar

Number.

Candleholders
Ljusstakar

Plates, Ashtrays
Fat, Askfat

Decanters
Karaffer

Miscellaneous
Övrigt

Slipning: En dekorativ teknik, där mönster slipas in med hjälp av vatten och sand. Skickliga slipare arbetar med spinnande järnhjul och andra hjälpmedel. En enda felaktig rörelse kan ruinera flera dagars arbete.

Gravering: En precisions-process där mönster slipas in i glaset med små roterande hjul. Hjulet fungerar som en tandläkarborr och biter sig in i glasytan. Gravören kan skapa mycket detaljerade bilder. Det tar tio års träning att lära sig graveringskonsten.

Kristall: Den högsta kvaliteten på glas. För att få kallas kristall måste minst 24% av glasmassan bestå av bly. Man kan se det på glasets speciella briljans och höra det på klangen.

Handblåst: Glas som är gjort på traditionellt vis av ett fyra- eller femmannalag. Flytande glas fångas upp på en glaspipa och blir sedan snurrat, blåst och format av handverktyg, blöta tidningar, stålplattor och centrifugalkraft. Det krävs enorm skicklighet och känslighet för att blåsa glas, något man bara lär sig genom träning.

Handmålat: Med en pensel och speciella glasfärgar målar konstnären mönster på glaset. Glaset bränns sedan så att färgen smälter och skapar en glaserad effekt. Den här tekniken kräver att hantverkaren är skicklig på att återge formgivarens idéer.

Cut: A decorative technique in which patterns are cut into cooled glass with water and sand. Cutters work at spinning iron wheels, grinding the glass slowly and carefully. One false move can ruin days of work.

Engraved: An extremely precise process in which designs are cut into glass with small high speed wheels. Working like a dental instrument, the wheel bites into the glass surface, covered with emery powder and oil. The engraver then applies a variety of strokes to produce the desired effect. It takes ten years of training to learn the art of engraving.

Full Lead Crystal: The finest quality of of glass you can buy. In order to be called Full Lead, at least 24% of its formula must be lead. You can tell it by its brilliance and softness. And by its distinctive deep "clink" when sounded.

Handblown: Glass that is made in the traditional manner by a team of four or five men. Molten glass is gathered on a blow pipe, then spun, blown, and shaped by handheld tools, wet newspapers, steel plates and centrifugal force. It takes tremendous skill and sensitivity to blow glass, learned only through experience.

Handpainted: With a brush and special glass paints, the artist paints the design on cooled glass. The piece is then fired, so the paint melts and produces an enameled effect. The technique requires the artist to be skilled at reproducing the designer's ideas directly onto the glass.

LES TECHNIQUES

Taillé: Une technique décorative par laquelle les dessins sont taillés dans le verre refroidi avec de l'eau et du sable. Les artisans utilisent des meules de fer tournantes, lentement et avec beaucoup de soin. Un faux mouvement peut ruiner des journées de travail.

Gravé: Un processus extrêmement précis par lequel les motifs sont tracés dans le verre avec de petites meules à grande vitesse. Comme la fraise du dentiste, la meule attaque la surface du verre recouverte de poudre émeri et d'huile. Un graveur arrive au résultat désiré en variant ses mouvements. Il faut dix ans pour devenir graveur.

Cristal au Plomb: C'est le verre de la plus haute qualité que l'on puisse acheter. Pour mériter l'appellation de Cristal au Plomb, il faut qu'il ait au moins 24% de teneur en plomb. On le reconnait par son éclat et sa douceur. Aussi par le tintement spécial qu'on entend quand on le fait vibrer.

Soufflé Main: Ce verre est fabriqué de façon traditionnelle par une équipe de quatre à cinq hommes. Le verre incandescent est rassemblé sur un chalumeau, puis filé, soufflé et formé avec des outils à main, des journaux humides, des plaques d'acier et la force centrifuge. Le soufflage du verre exige dextérité et délicatesse et nécessite une longue expérience.

Peint Main: Avec un pinceau et des peintures spéciales pour le verre, l'artiste peint le motif sur le verre refroidi. La pièce est cuite, la peinture fond et donne un effet émaillé. L'artiste doit savoir reproduire directement sur le verre les idées du designer.

DIE TECHNIKEN

Geschliffen: Mit Wasser und Sand werden dekorative Muster in kaltes Glas eingeschliffen. Schleifer drehen eiserne Räder und zerkleinern das Glas langsam und vorsichtig. Mit nur einer falschen Bewegung können Tage von Arbeit ruiniert werden.

Gravieren: Ein extrem präziser Vorgang. Wie ein Zahnbohrer gravieren schnell drehende Stifte, die mit Öl und Schmiergel bedeckt sind, Muster in die Glasoberfläche ein. Mit einer Vielfalt von Schliffen produziert der Graveur den gewünschten Effekt. Die Ausbildung für die Kunst des Gravierens beträgt zehn Jahre.

Gefüllte Blei Kristalle: Die beste Qualität von Glas. Gefülltes Blei muss einen Mindestgehalt von 24% Blei in der Formel enthalten. Man erkennt es am Glanz, der Geschmeidigkeit und dem tiefen Klang.

Handblasen: In traditioneller Weise wird das Glas in Zusammenarbeit von fünf Männern hergestellt. Geschmolzenes Glas läuft durch ein Glasrohr, wird ausgezogen, geblasen, geformt mit Formwerkzeugen und feuchtem Zeitungspapier und Zentrifugalkraft. Das Freihandblasen erfordert enorme Fähigkeit und Feingefühl und wird nur durch Erfahrung gelernt.

Handbemalung: Der Künstler bemalt das kalte Glas mit Pinsel und besonderen Glasfarben. Danach wird das Glas gebrannt, damit die Farbe einschmilzt. Der Künstler reproduziert die Ideen der Entwürfe auf das Glas.

U

THE UNIQUE PIECES AND LIMITED EDITIONS

Det här är speciella verk. Ögonblick av inspiration fångade i glas för evigt. Var och en av Kosta Bodas formgivare har här sin chans att uttrycka sig själv. Därför är resultaten inte nödvändigtvis praktiska, utan "bara" skapade för att njutas av.

Unikaten är just – unika. Men liknande verk kan vara tillgängliga om det på bilden redan är sålt.

Limited Editions tillverkas i begränsad upplaga. Varje verk är handblåst, signerat och numrerat av konstnären själv. Många är handmålade. Kosta Boda Unikat och Limited Editions finns i bättre butiker och på gallerier.

Ce sont des pièces spéciales. Des moments d'inspiration fixés pour toujours dans le verre. C'est là que chaque designer de Kosta Boda laisse courir au maximum son imagination. Il n'en resulte pas nécessairement des objets pratiques et commerciaux, mais plutôt embus d'une certaine magie.

Les Unique Pieces qui sont les modèles de ces photographies sont uniques. Ce sont des oeuvres d'art qui ne sont pas reproduites. Toutefois, on peut se procurer des pièces similaires si celle de la photo est déjà vendue.

Les oeuvres des Limited Edition existent en quantité limitée. Chaque pièce est souflée à la main, beaucoup sont peintes à la main et chacune est signée et numérotée par l'artiste.

Ces Unique Pieces et Limited Editions de Kosta Boda sont vendues dans les meilleurs magasins et les galeries d'art.

These are special pieces. Moments of inspiration frozen in glass forever.

Each of the Kosta Boda designers has his chance here to fully express himself. So the results are not necessarily practical and commercial, but more magical.

The Unique Pieces that appear in each of these photographs are one of a kind. Unduplicated works of art. However, similar pieces may be available if the one pictured is already sold.

The Limited Edition works are available in limited quantities. Each piece is handblown, many are hand painted, and each is signed and numbered by the artist.

The Kosta Boda Unique Pieces and Limited Editions will be available in finer stores and galleries.

Es sind aussergewöhliche Werke. Ewig im Glas eingefrorene Momente von Inspiration.
Diese Kunstgegenstände sind nicht kommerziell, sondern bieten dem Entwerfer vollen, schöpferischen Ausdruck.

Die Unique Pieces sind einzigartige Kunstgegenstände. Sollte eines dieser Kunstwerke verkauft sein, sind gleichartige Stücke erhältich.

Die Kunstgegenstände der Limited Edition stehen in beschränkten Auflagen zur Verfügung. Jedes Stück wird vom Künstler numeriert und signiert, handgeblasen und sehr viele sogar handbemalt.

Unique Pieces und Limited Editions von Kosta Boda sind in Galerien und Kaufhäusern zum Verkauf angeboten.

Monica Backström

Designer

På 60-talet lade Monica Backström in gem i kristall. På 70-talet började hon göra ägg. Nu på 80-talet fascineras hon av yttre rymden, och hennes skulpturer har tagit form av flygande tefat i kristall.

In the Sixties, she put paperclips in crystal. In the Seventies she started making eggs. Now in the Eighties, she is fascinated by outer space—and her shapes have taken on the look of crystal UFOs.

In den sechziger Jahren legte sie Büroklammern in Kristalle. In den siebziger Jahren fing sie an Glaseier zu gestalten. Jetzt in den achtziger Jahren ist sie vom Weltall fasziniert und ihre Formen nehmen die Gestalt von kristallenen, fliegenden Untertassen an.

Dans les années soixante elle plaçait des trombones dans le cristal. Dans les années soixante-dix elle a commencé à faire des objets en forme d'oeufs. Maintenant, dans les années quatre-vingt, elle est fascinée par l'espace et ses créations ressemblent à des OVNI en cristal.

Lisa Bauer

Designer

Lisa Bauer är känd som "Blommornas Drottning."
Hennes graverade skålar avslöjar hennes djupa botaniska kunskap. Varje skål visar inte bara hennes talang som illustratör, utan också hennes arbete som landskapsarkitekt.

She is known in Sweden as the "Queen of Flowers."
Her engraved bowls, bearing her intimate knowledge of flora, are legendary. Each one carries not only her experience as an illustrator, but her work as a landscape planner, too.

In Schweden ist sie bekannt als die «Königin der Blumen.» Ihre Schalen zeigen ein vertrautes Wissen der Pflanzenwelt. Jede Schale zeigt ihre Erfahrung als Illustrator und ihre Arbeit als Landschaftsplaner.

En Suède elle est connue sous le nom de "Reine des Fleurs." Ses coupes, qui portent la marque de sa profonde connaissance de la flore, sont légendaires. Chacune est non seulement la preuve de son expérience d'illustratrice, mais aussi de paysagiste.

Bengt Edenfalk
Designer

När man sitter i Bengt Edenfalks soldränkta ateljé, märker man att det ligger små bitar av färgat glas överallt. Dessa skapar dragen av färg i hans senaste verk. Hans glaskonst delar livfullheten med hans färgglada konfettimålningar.

When you sit in Bengt Edenfalk's sunlit studio, you notice small pieces of colored glass everywhere. These create the inky strokes of color on his latest pieces. They share the vibrancy of his colorful, confettied paintings.

In Bengt Edenfalk's sonnigem Studio sieht man kleine, bunte Glasgegenstände überall. Seine Glasgegenstände, wie mit kräftigen Pinselstrichen in das Glas eingeschmolzen, vibrieren mit seinen farbenfreudigen Gemälden.

Lorsqu'on est assis dans le studio baigné de soleil de Bengt Edenfalk, on peut remarquer partout de petits morceaux de verre coloré. C'est avec ces morceaux de verre qu'il obtient l'effet de couleurs d'encre dans ses dernières créations. On y retrouve la sensibilité de ses peintures à confettis pleines d'originalité.

Anna Ehrner

Designer

Det går en behagfull linje i allt som Anna Ehrner designar – vare sig det är ett Line martiniglas, en Blue Sky tallrik eller en av hennes unika skulpturer.

There is a graceful line running through everything she designs – whether it is a Line martini glass, a Blue Sky plate, or one of her unique sculptures.

Jede Form zeigt eine anmutige Linie, das Line Martini Glas, ein Blue Sky Teller, oder eine aussergewöhnliche Skulptur.

Tout ce qu'elle dessine porte l'empreinte d'une ligne gracieuse, que ce soit un verre pour cocktail Line, une assiette Blue Sky, ou l'une de ses sculptures uniques.

Ulrika Hydman-Vallien

Designer

Ulrika Hydman-Vallien tar ett nyttoföremål, som ett vinglas, och snurrar en orm runt foten. Hon skapar ett glas fullt av elaka kvinnor och fåglar med manshuvuden. Hennes värld är fylld av fantasi och sagor, en djärv och spännande värld.

She takes a useful object, like a drinking glass, and winds a snake around the stem. She creates art glass full of nasty women and manheaded birds. Hers is a world of fantasy and fairy tales that has a daring and joyous spirit.

SIE NIMMT EINEN NÜTZLICHEN GEGENSTAND, Z.B. EIN TRINKGLAS UND WINDET EINE SCHLANGE UM DEN STIEL. SIE GESTALTET KUNSTGLÄSER AUF DENEN HÄSSLICHE FRAUEN UND VÖGEL MIT MENSCHENKÖPFEN ABGEBILDET SIND. EINE WELT VOLL MÄRCHEN, PHANTASIE UND FREUDIGEM GEIST.

ELLE CHOISIT UN OBJET UTILE, COMME UN VERRE À BOIRE, PUIS ENROULE UN SERPENT AUTOUR DU PIED. ELLE CRÉE DES VERRES D'ART QUI ARBORENT DES FEMMES À L'AIR MENAÇANT ET DES OISEAUX À TÊTES D'HOMMES. ELLE VIT DANS UN MONDE DE FANTAISIE ET DE CONTES DE FÉES, PLEIN D'AUDACE ET D'ALLÉGRESSE.

Gun Lindblad
Designer

Skarpa kanter och räta vinklar utmärker Gun Lindblads arbete. Gun säger: "Jag tycker om enkelhet och tydliga former, rena linjer kombinerade, om möjligt, med stark färg"

Sharp edges and right angles define her work. She says, "I like simplicity and well-defined shapes, purity of line combined, if possible, with strong color."

Spitze Kanten und rechte Winkel definieren ihre Arbeit. Sie sagt: «Ich mag Einfachheit, klar definierte Formen und Linien, kräftige Farben.»

Ses oeuvres sont marquées par des bords tranchants et des angles droits. Elle déclare: "J'aime la simplicité et les formes bien définies, une pureté de ligne qui s'ajoute, si possible, à une couleur intense."

Christian von Sydow

Designer

Christian von Sydow arbetar med kraftiga färger och klassiska former – design som förenar element från förr med nutida form och färg.

He works with potent colors and classic shapes – designs that combine elements from the past with something entirely contemporary.

Er arbeitet mit kräftigen Farben und klassischen Formen. Entwürfe, die Elemente der Vergangenheit mit der Gegenwart verbinden.

Il emploie des couleurs vives et des formes classiques – des créations qui allient des éléments du passé à quelque chose de tout à fait contemporain.

Bertil Vallien

Designer

I Bertil Valliens gjutna skepp flyter evighetssymboler omkring, som om de vore fångade i en tidskapsel. Mumier, trappor, forntida lämningar ligger och väntar på att bli upptäckta. Hans arbeten sätter minnet i rörelse på ett oförklarligt sätt.

In his sandcasted ships symbols of eternity float, as if caught in a time capsule. Mummies, stairs, fosillized bits of ancient life lie waiting to be discovered. His work stirs the memory in an unexplainable way.

In seinen sandgegossenen Schiffen schweben Symbole der Ewigkeit, wie in einer Zeitkapsel festgehalten. Uraltes Leben, versteinerte Mumien und Treppenstufen warten hier, um entdeckt zu werden. Seine Kunstwerke berühren die Erinnerung in unerklärlicher Weise.

Dans ses bateaux moulés flottent des symboles de l'éternité comme s'ils étaient captés dans une capsule témoin. Des momies, des escaliers, des morceaux d'antiquité fossilisés attendent d'être découverts. Il est surprenant comme ses oeuvres stimulent la mémoire.

Göran Wärff

Designer

Det är Göran Wärffs fascination av vatten och dess rörelse som återkommer gång på gång i hans arbete. "Glas lever. Det ändrar sig hela tiden," säger han. "Precis när man tror att man har fångat det, ändrar det sig igen.

It is his fascination with water and its movement that shows up again and again in his work. "Glass is alive. It changes all the time" he says. "Just when you think you've mastered it, it changes all over again."

Es ist die Begeisterung für das Meer und der rhytmischen Bewegung des Meeres, die in seiner Arbeit wieder und wieder erscheint. Er sagt: «Glas ist lebendig und verändert sich mit der Zeit, gerade wenn man denkt das Glas ist gemeistert, verändert es sich schon wieder.»

Il est fasciné par l'eau et ses mouvements et c'est ce qui ressort continuellement dans ses oeuvres. "Le verre est vivant. Il change tout le temps," dit-il. "C'est quand on pense l'avoir maîtrisé qu'il change à nouveau."

THE COLLECTION

Här hittar du gamla favoriter och nya idéer. Det som gjort Kosta Boda känt och omtyckt över hela världen. Vissa sidor presenterar hela familjer, som t.ex. Line och Chateau med martiniglas, vinglas, oljelampor, skålar, allt. På andra sidor finner du enstaka "individer," som skålar, vaser etc.

Varje del har blivit utvald för att den är vacker, omtyckt och för att den representerar det som Kosta Boda står för.

On y trouve des pièces qui sont les favorites depuis longtemps, mais aussi de nouvelles idées. Le cristal et le verre que Kosta Boda vend dans le monde entier.

Dans ces quelques pages vous verrez des lignes entières, comme Line et Chateau avec des verres pour cocktail, des verres à vin, des lampes à l'huile, des coupes, de tout en somme. Aux autres pages, des objets uniques en eux-mêmes.

Nous les avons choisis parce que chacun d'eux est très beau, très apprécié du public et représente l'essence même de Kosta Boda.

Here you will find old favorites and new ideas. The crystal and glass that Kosta Boda sells all over the world.

Some pages present whole families, like Line or Chateau, with martini glasses, wine glasses, oil lamps, bowls, everything. Other pages present single pieces that exist in their own right.

Each has been chosen because it is beautiful, popular, and because it represents what Kosta Boda is all about.

Hier findet man alte Favoriten und neue Ideen. Das Kristall und Glas das Kosta Boda überall in der Welt verkauft.

Manche Exemplare, Martini Gläser, Weingläser, Öllampen und Schalen werden zu Familien wie Line oder Chateau geliefert. Andere existieren als kostbare Einzelstücke.

Jedes Stück wurde wegen seiner Formschönheit und Popularität gewählt und representiert den Namen Kosta Boda.

ADMIRAL

DESIGN: BERTIL VALLIEN. HANDBLOWN. HANDBLÅST

20162
DECANTER, 17¼OZ, 1/BOX
KARAFF, 50 CL 1/KART
H: 10". 255 MM

Anemone

Design: Kjell Engman. Handblown. Handblåst

48507
Vase, 1/box
Vas, 1/kart
H: 8". 200 mm

48506
Vase, 1/box
Vas, 1/kart
H: 7". 170 mm

48508
VASE, 1/BOX
VAS, 1/KART
H: 9". 230 MM

48505
VASE, 1/BOX
VAS, 1/KART
H: 4¾". 120 MM

Aqua

Design: Anna Ehrner. Handblown. Handblåst

48605
Vase, 1/box
Vas, 1/kart
H: 11". 280 mm

48602
Vase, 1/box
Vas, 1/kart
H: 6¼". 160 mm

48603
VASE, 1/BOX
VAS, 1/KART
H: 8". 200 MM

48604
VASE, 1/BOX
VAS, 1/KART
H: 9½". 240 MM

48601
VASE, 1/BOX
VAS, 1/KART
H: 4¾". 120 MM

AQUA BLUE

DESIGN: ANNA EHRNER. HANDBLOWN. HANDBLÅST

48607
VASE, 1/BOX
VAS, 1/KART
H: 4¾". 120 MM

48609
VASE, 1/BOX
VAS, 1/KART
H: 8". 200 MM

48608
VASE, 1/BOX
VAS, 1/KART
H: 6¼". 160 MM

48611
VASE, 1/BOX
VAS, 1/KART
H: 11". 280 MM

48610
VASE, 1/BOX
VAS, 1/KART
H: 9½". 240 MM

Atlantic

Design: Göran Wärff. Full Lead Crystal, Handblown, Cut. Kristall, Handblåst, Slipad

58006
Bowl, round
Skål, rund.
H: 4¾". 120 mm
Ø: 8½". 215 mm

48007
Vase, oval
Vas, oval
H: 7½". 190 mm
Ø: 7¼" × 5¼". 180 × 130 mm

48006
Vase, round
Vas, rund
H: 9½". 240 mm
Ø: 4¼". 110 mm

Not shown:
Visas ej:

58005
Bowl, round
Skål, rund
H: 4″
H: 105 mm
Ø: 6½″
Ø: 170 mm

58008
Bowl, oval
Skål, oval
H: 4¾″
H: 120 mm
Ø: 9½ × 6¼″
Ø: 240 ×
160 mm

58009
Bowl, oval
Skål, oval
H: 6½″. 165 mm
Ø: 8¾ × 6″. 225 × 150 mm

48005
Vase, round
Vas, rund
H: 7½″. 190 mm
Ø: 5½″. 140 mm

58007
Bowl, oval
Skål, oval
H: 4″. 105 mm
Ø: 7½″ × 5″. 190 × 130 mm

Aveny

Design: Bengt Edenfalk. Full Lead Crystal, Handblown, Cut. Kristall, Handblåst. Slipad

48458
Vase
Vas
H: 7¼". 185 mm

48459
Vase
Vas
H: 9". 230 mm

Astoria

Design: Rolf Sinnemark. Full Lead Crystal, Handblown. Kristall, Handblåst

48402
Vase. Vas
H: 6½". 170 mm

48403
Vase. Vas
H: 9½". 240 mm

48401
Vase. Vas
H: 8½". 220 mm

Bellis

Design: Kjell Blomberg

66045
Candle Ring, 1/box
Ljuskrans, 1/kart
Ø: 10". 250 mm

BARCLAY

DESIGN: GUN LINDBLAD. FULL LEAD CRYSTAL, HANDBLOWN, CUT. KRISTALL, HANDBLÅST, SLIPAD

48301	58301	48303
VASE	BOWL	VASE
VAS	SKÅL	VAS
H: 8¼". 210 MM	Ø; 6¼" 160 MM	H: 13¾". 350 MM

58302
Bowl
Skål
Ø: 8½". 220 mm

48302
Vase
Vas
H: 10½". 270 mm

Blanc Rouge Rosé

Design: Anna Ehrner. Handblown. Handblåst

88514
Carafe, 30 oz. 1/box
Karaff, 85 cl, 1/kart
H: 10¼". 260 mm
Ø: 2¾". 70 mm

88516
Carafe, 35 oz, 1/box
Karaff, 100 cl, 1/kart
H: 9". 230 mm
Ø: 2¾". 70 mm

88515
CARAFE, 30 OZ, 1/BOX
KARAFF, 85 CL, 1/KART
H: 9½". 240 MM
Ø: 3". 75 MM

Blue Spice

Design: Ulrica Hydman-Vallien. Handblown. Handblåst

58603
Bowl, 1/Box
Skål, 1/Kart
H: 6¼". 160 mm
Ø: 9½". 240 mm

58601
Bowl, 1/Box
Skål, 1/Kart
H: 4¾". 120 mm
Ø: 6½". 165 mm

NOT SHOWN:
VISAS EJ:

58602
BOWL, 1/BOX
SKÅL, 1/KART
H: 5½″
H: 140 MM
Ø: 8″
Ø: 205 MM

98609
GLASS, 6¼ OZ, 1/BOX
GLAS, 18 CL, 1/KART
H: 6¼″. 160 MM

88603
JUG, 53 OZ, 1/BOX
KANNA, 150 CL, 1/KART
H: 8″. 200 MM

Bouquet

Design: Signe Persson-Melin. Handblown, Cut. Handblåst, Slipad

94210
Wine tasting glass, 2½ oz, 24/box
Vinprovarglas, 7 cl, 24/kart
H: 6½", 170 mm

94199
Decanter, 35 oz, 1/box
Karaff, 100 cl, 1/kart
H: 11½", 295 mm

94207
WINE, 12¼ OZ, 24/BOX
VIN, 35 CL, 24/KART
H: 6¼". 160 MM

94217
WINE, 3½ OZ, 24/BOX
VIN, 10 CL, 24/KART
H: 4¾". 120 MM

94206
WINE, 7 OZ, 24/BOX
VIN, 20 CL, 24/KART
H: 7". 175 MM

94218
WINE, 3 OZ. 24/BOX
VIN, 8 CL, 24/KART
H: 4½". 115 MM

Caesar

Design: Göran Wärff. Full Lead Crystal, Handblown, Cut. Kristall, Handblåst, Slipad

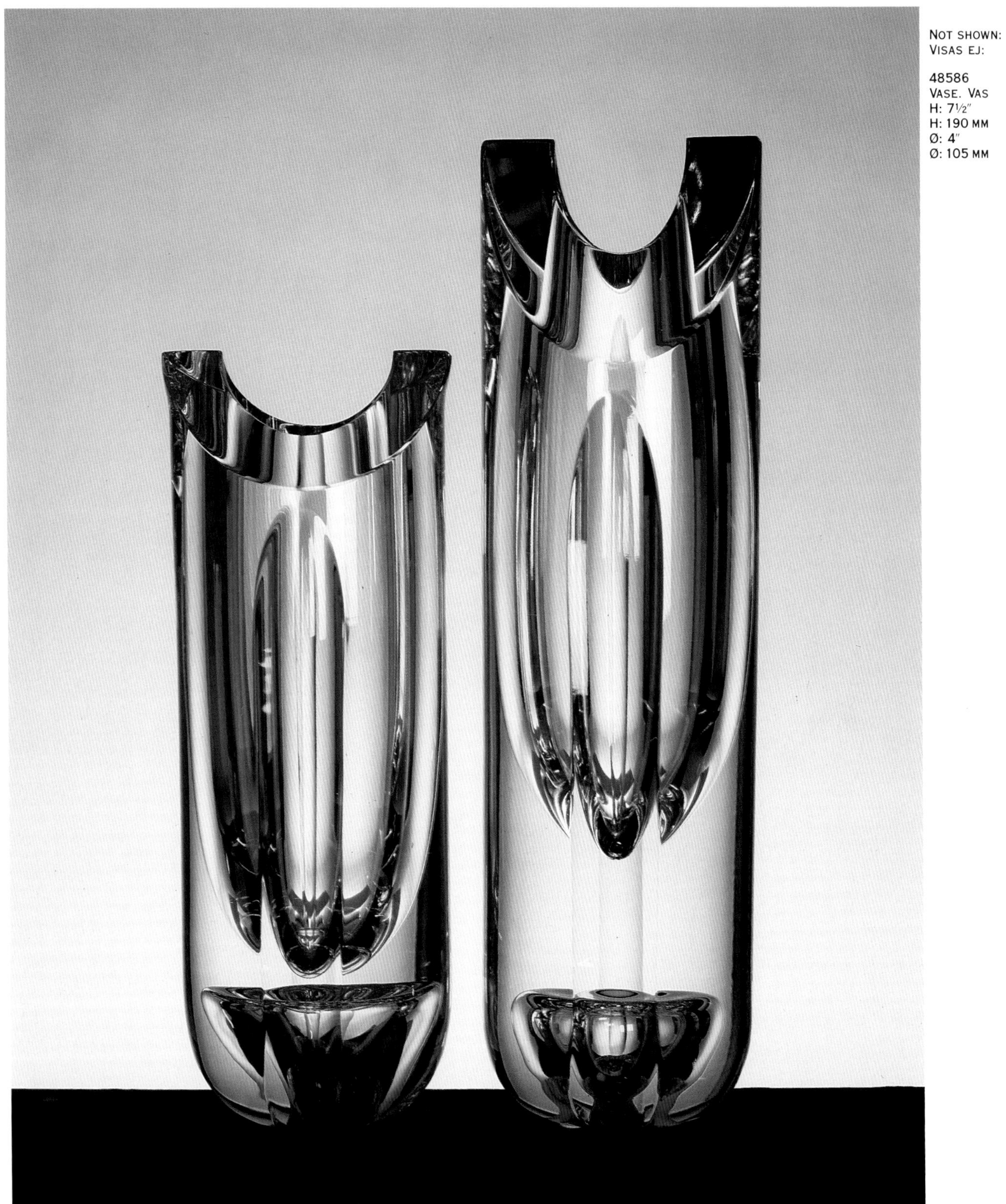

Not shown:
Visas ej:

48586
Vase. Vas
H: 7½″
H: 190 mm
Ø: 4″
Ø: 105 mm

48587
Vase
Vas
H: 9½″. 240 mm
Ø: 3½″. 90 mm

48588
Vase
Vas
H: 11¾″. 300 mm
Ø: 3½″. 90 mm

Chess

Design: Göran Wärff. Full Lead Crystal, Handblown, Cut. Kristall, Handblåst, Slipad

88501
Decanter, 23 oz
Karaff, 65 cl
H: 7¼". 185 mm

CAMERA

DESIGN: GUN LINDBLAD. FULL LEAD CRYSTAL, HANDBLOWN, CUT. KRISTALL, HANDBLÅST, SLIPAD

48590
VASE
VAS
H: 7¼". 185 MM
Ø: 4". 100 MM

58590
BOWL
SKÅL
H: 4". 100 MM
Ø: 4¾". 120 MM

48589
VASE
VAS
H: 6½". 170 MM
Ø: 3". 75 MM

48591
VASE
VAS
H: 8½". 220 MM
Ø: 4". 100 MM

58589
BOWL
SKÅL
H: 3". 75 MM
Ø: 3½". 90 MM

Canasta

Design: Rolf Sinnemark. Full Lead Crystal, Handblown. Kristall, Handblåst

58558
Bowl
Skål
H: 2¾". 70 mm
Ø: 8". 200 mm

48559
Vase
Vas
H:8½". 220 mm
Ø: 5". 130 mm

48560
Vase
Vas
H: 8". 200 mm
Ø: 3½". 90 mm

Not shown:
Visas ej:

48558
Vase. Vas
H: 8½″
H: 220 mm
Ø: 5″
Ø: 130 mm

58559
Bowl
Skål
H: 3″
H: 75 mm
Ø: 11¾″
Ø: 300 mm

58561
Bowl. Skål
H: 4½″
H: 115 mm
Ø: 8″
Ø: 200 mm

78558
Ashtray
Askfat
Ø: 4¾″
Ø: 120 mm

78559
Ashtray
Askfat
Ø: 6¼″
Ø: 160 mm

78560
Ashtray
Askfat
H: 2¾″
H: 70 mm
Ø: 8½″
Ø: 220 mm

68558
Candlestick
Ljusstake
H: 3″. 75 mm
Ø: 5″. 125 mm

48561
Vase
Vas
H: 8″. 200 mm
Ø: 3½″. 90 mm

58560
Bowl
Skål
H: 4″. 100 mm
Ø: 6¼″. 160 mm

Captain

Design: Monica Backström. Handblown. Handblåst

22149
O F, 7 oz, 2/box
O F, 20 cl, 2/kart
H: 3¼". 85 mm
Ø. 0". 75 mm

88527
Ice Jug, 38 oz, 1/box
Iskanna, 110 cl, 1/kart
H: 8¼". 210 mm
Ø: 4¼". 110 mm

22151
COCKTAIL 5¼ OZ, 2/BOX
COCKTAIL, 15 CL, 2/KART
H: 3". 75 MM
Ø: 2¾" 70 MM

22150
DOF, 9 OZ, 2/BOX
DOF, 25 CL, 2/KART
H: 3¾". 95 MM
Ø: 3¼". 85 MM

22125
AQUAVIT, 2 OZ, 2/BOX
SNAPS, 5 CL, 2/KART
H: 3". 75 MM
Ø: 1½". 40 MM

22146
HIGHBALL, 12¼ OZ, 2/BOX
GROGGLAS, 35 CL, 2/KART
H: 6". 150 MM
Ø: 2¾". 70 MM

Captain

Design: Monica Backström. Handblown. Handblåst

22181
Ice bucket, 31 oz, 1/box
Ishink, 90 cl, 1/kart
H: 10¼". 260 mm
Ø: 5". 130 mm

58623
Bowl, 1/box
Skål, 1/kart
H: 2½". 65 mm
Ø: 5". 130 mm

22162
Decanter, 35 oz, 1/box
Karaff, 100 cl, 1/kart
H: 10". 250 mm

NOT SHOWN:
VISAS EJ:

58639
BOWL, 1/BOX
SKÅL, 1/KART
H: 4″
H: 100 MM
Ø: 10¼″
Ø: 260 MM

58527
BOWL, 1/BOX
SKÅL, 1/KART
H: 2¾″. 70 MM
Ø: 4″. 100 MM

58624
BOWL, 1/BOX
SKÅL, 1/KART
H: 4″. 100 MM
Ø: 8½″. 215 MM

CARDINAL

DESIGN: GUN LINDBLAD. FULL LEAD CRYSTAL, HANDBLOWN, CUT. KRISTALL, HANDBLÅST, SLIPAD

48425
VASE
VAS
H: 7". 180 MM

58424
BOWL
SKÅL
D: 6¼ x 6¼". 160 x 160 MM

48427
VASE
VAS
H: 10¼". 265 MM

48424
VASE
VAS
H: 6¼". 160 MM

48426
VASE
VAS
H: 8½". 220 MM

Carmen

Design: Gun Lindblad. Full Lead Crystal, Handblown. Kristall, Handblåst

Vase. Vas
H: 9". 225 mm
Ø: 4". 105 mm
48573 Orange. Orange
48570 Turquoise. Turkos

Vase. Vas
H: 7". 180 mm
Ø: 3". 75 mm
48572 Orange. Orange
48569 Turquoise. Turkos

Bowl. Skål
H: 2½". 65 mm
Ø: 3½". 90 mm
58572 Orange. Orange
58569 Turquoise. Turkos

Bowl. Skål
H: 4¾". 120 mm
Ø: 4". 100 mm
58573 Orange. Orange
58570 Turquoise. Turkos

Bowl. Skål
H: 3¾". 95 mm
Ø: 6". 155 mm
58574 Orange. Orange
58571 Turquoise. Turkos

Cascade

Design: Bengt Edenfalk. Full Lead Crystal, Handblown, Cut. Kristall, Handblåst, Slipad

48360
Vase
Vas
H: 7¼". 185 mm
Ø: 4". 100 mm

58360
Bowl
Skål
Ø: 5". 130 mm

58362
Bowl
Skål
Ø: 8¼". 210 mm

78360
ASHTRAY
ASKFAT
Ø: 6″. 150 MM

48361
VASE
VAS
H: 9″. 230 MM
Ø: 4½″. 115 MM

58361
BOWL
SKÅL
Ø: 6½″. 170 MM

Cavalcade

Design: Bengt Edenfalk. Full Lead Crystal, Handblown, Cut. Kristall, Handblåst, Slipad

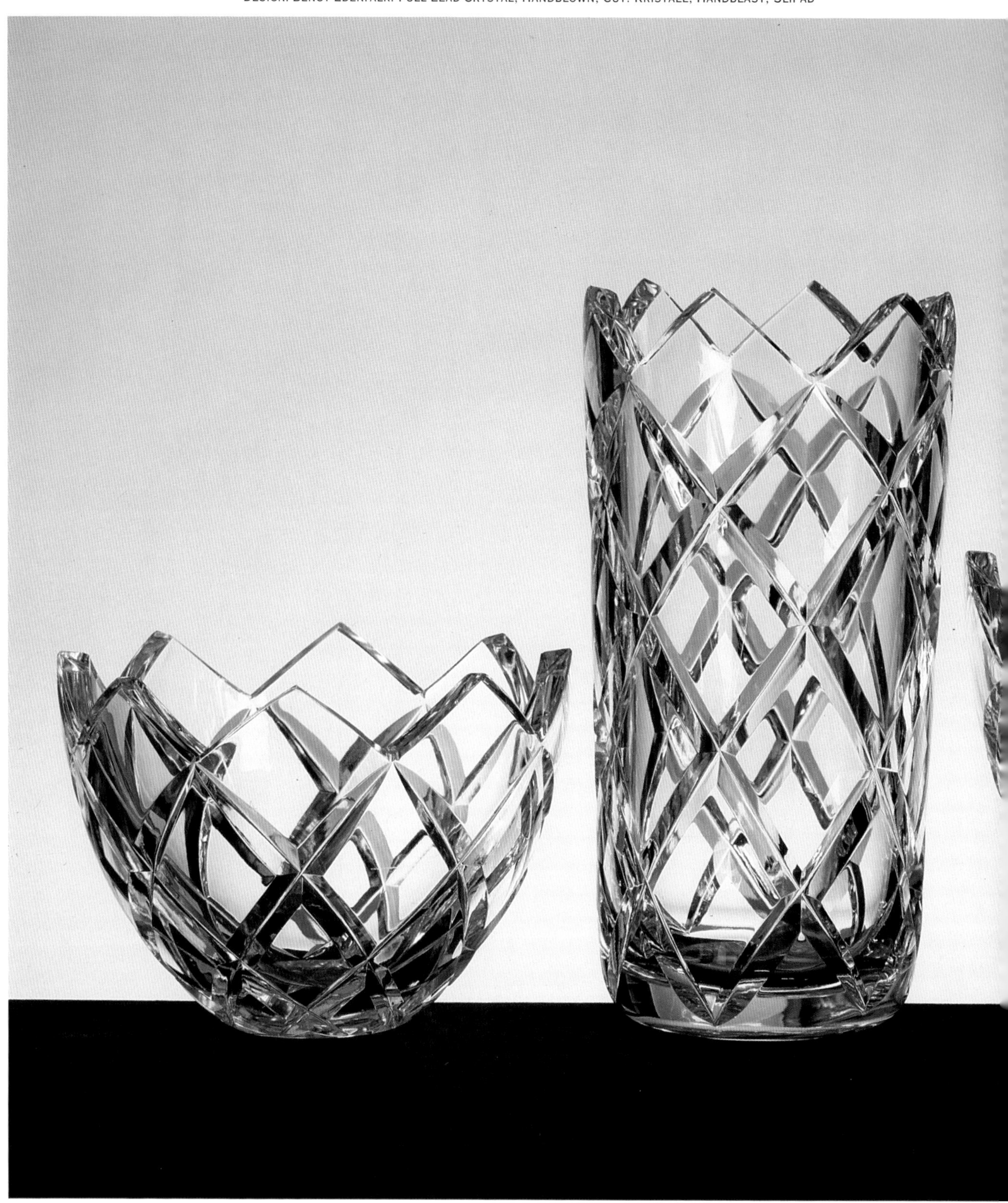

58431
Bowl
Skål
Ø: 6½". 170 mm

48431
Vase
Vas
H: 9", 230 mm

Not shown:
Visas ej:

58430
Bowl. Skål
Ø: 5″
Ø: 130 mm

58432
Bowl
Skål
Ø: 8¼″. 210 mm

48430
Vase
Vas
H: 7¼″. 185 mm

Charade

Design: Bengt Edenfalk. Full Lead Crystal. Kristall

98584
Block
Block
H: 6". 150 mm
Ø: 3¾". 95 mm

98583
Block
Block
H: 4". 100 mm
Ø: 3". 75 mm

98585
Block
Block
H: 4¾". 120 mm
Ø: 3½". 90 mm

Not shown:
Visas ej:

98586
Block
Block
H: 6″
H: 150 mm
Ø: 5″
Ø: 130 mm

98589
Block
Block
2 × 4 × 6¼″
55 × 105 ×
160 mm

98588
Block
Block
2½ × 2½ × 5½″
60 × 60 × 140 mm

98587
Block
Block
H: 4″. 100 mm
Ø: 4½″. 115 mm

Charm

Design: Ulrica Hydman-Vallien. Handblown. Handblåst.

48584	58584	48585
Vase	Bowl	Vase
Vas	Skål	Vas
H: 8". 200 mm	H: 3¼". 85 mm	H: 10½". 270 mm
Ø: 3½". 90 mm	Ø: 3¼". 85 mm	Ø: 4¾". 120 mm

58585
Bowl
Skål
H: 4½". 115 mm
Ø: 4¼". 110 mm

58586
Bowl
Skål
H: 8". 200 mm
Ø: 9½". 240 mm

Chateau

Design: Bertil Vallien. Handblown. Handblåst

21206
Wine, 7 oz, 2/box
Vin, 20 cl, 2/kart
H: 7½". 190 mm
Ø: 3¼". 85 mm

21208
Wine, 10¼ oz, 2/box
Vin, 30 cl, 2/kart
H: 8¼". 210 mm
Ø: 3¾". 95 mm

21262
Carafe, 39 oz, 1/box
Vinkaraff, 110 cl, 1/kart
H: 10½". 270 mm

21205	21201	21207	21203	21204
WINE, 5¼ OZ, 2/BOX	WINE, 1¼ OZ, 2/BOX	WINE, 9 OZ, 2/BOX	WINE, 2½ OZ, 2/BOX	WINE, 3½ OZ, 2/BOX
VIN, 15 CL, 2/KART	VIN, 4 CL, 2/KART	VIN, 25 CL, 2/KART	VIN, 7½ CL, 2/KART	VIN, 10 CL, 2/KART
H: 6½". 170 MM	H: 4¾". 120 MM	H: 8". 200 MM	H: 5¾". 145 MM	H: 6". 150 MM
Ø: 3". 75 MM	Ø: 2". 50 MM	Ø: 3½". 90 MM	Ø: 2¼". 60 MM	Ø: 2½". 65 MM

Chateau

Design: Bertil Vallien. Handblown. Handblåst

21233	21225	88427	21235	21221
Martini, 5¼ oz, 2/box	Aquavit, 2 oz, 2/box	Jug, 42 oz, 1/box	Dessert bowl, 9 oz, 2/box	Champagne flute, 5¼ oz, 2/box
Martini, 15 cl, 2/kart	Snaps, 5 cl, 2/kart	Kanna, 120 cl, 1/kart	Dessertskål, 25 cl, 2/kart	Champagne hög, 15 cl, 2/kart
H: 6". 150 mm	H: 5¾". 145 mm	H: 7". 180 mm	H: 4¼". 110 mm	H: 9". 225 mm
Ø: 4". 100 mm	Ø: 2". 50 mm		Ø: 4". 100 mm	Ø: 2¼". 60 mm

21222
CHAMPAGNE BOWL, 5¼ OZ, 2/BOX
CHAMPAGNE SKÅL, 15 CL, 2/KART
H: 5¾". 145 MM
Ø: 3¾". 95 MM

21261
DECANTER, 39 OZ, 1/BOX
KARAFF, 110 CL, 1/KART
H: 9½". 240 MM

21231
COGNAC, 5¼ OZ, 2/BOX
COGNAC 15 CL, 2/KART
H: 4½". 115 MM
Ø: 2". 50 MM

21232
COGNAC, 10¼ OZ, 2/BOX
COGNAC, 30 CL, 2/KART
H: 5¼". 135 MM
Ø: 2". 50 MM

Chateau

Design: Bertil Vallien. Handblown. Handblåst

21289	21290	21288	21281
D O F, 14 oz, 2/box	Highball, 16 oz, 2/box	O F, 10 oz, 2/box	Ice bucket, 44 oz, 1/box
D O F, 40 cl, 2/kart	Grogg, 45 cl, 2/kart	O F, 28 cl, 2/kart	Ishink, 125 cl, 1/kart
H: 3" 75 mm	H: 6". 150 mm	H: 3". 75 mm	H: 5". 130 mm
Ø: 3" 75 mm	Ø: 2¼". 60 mm	Ø: 3". 75 mm	Ø: 5½". 140 mm

21293	21287	48268	21291	21292
HIGHBALL, 12¼ OZ, 2/BOX	COCKTAIL, 6¼ OZ, 2/BOX	VASE, 1/BOX	O F, 7 OZ, 2/BOX	D O F, 10¼ OZ, 2/BOX
GROGGLAS, 35 CL, 2/KART	COCKTAIL, 18 CL, 2/KART	VAS, 1/KART	O F, 20 CL, 2/KART	D O F, 30 CL, 2/KART
H: 6¼". 160 MM	H: 2½". 65 MM	H: 9½". 245 MM	H: 3¼". 85 MM	H: 4". 100 MM
Ø: 2½". 65 MM	Ø: 2½". 65 MM		Ø: 3". 75 MM	Ø: 3". 75 MM

Chateau

Design: Bertil Vallien. Handblown. Handblåst

48271	48267	48270	58267
Vase, 1/box	Vase, 1/box	Vase, 1/box	Bowl, 1/box
Vas, 1/kart	Vas, 1/kart	Vas, 1/kart	Skål, 1/kart
H: 11¼". 285 mm	H: 6". 150 mm	H: 8". 200 mm	Ø: 8". 200 mm

Not shown:
Visas ej:

58268
Bowl, 1/box
Skål, 1/kart
Ø: 9½"
Ø: 240 mm

58161
Bowl, footed, 1/box
Skål, på fot, 1/kart
Ø: 8". 200 mm

48269
Vase, 1/box
Vas, 1/kart
H: 7". 175 mm

Christmas Ornaments

Design: Bertil Vallien

F	G	H	I	J
97746	97691	97692	97769	97856
Bird, 1/box	Bell, 1/box	Angel, 1/box	Reindeer, 1/box	Father Christmas, 1/box
Fågel, 1/kart	Klocka, 1/kart	Ängel, 1/kart	Ren, 1/kart	Tomte, 1/kart
H. 1¼". 35 mm	H. 2¾". 70 mm	H. 2¾". 70 mm	H. 2". 50 mm	H. 3". 75 mm

A
97693
Star, 1/box
Stjärna, 1/kart
H: 2¾". 70 mm

B
97694
Christmas goat, 1/box
Julbock, 1/kart
H: 2½". 65 mm

C
97768
Apple, 1/box
Äpple, 1/kart
H: 2¼". 60 mm

D
97770
Father Christmas w. sleigh, 1/box
Tomte i släde, 1/kart
H: 3". 75 mm

E
97857
Angel, 1/box
Ängel, 1/kart
H: 2¾". 70 mm

Not shown:
Visas ej:

97664
Heart,
12/box
Hjärta,
12/kart
H: 2". 50 mm

K
97690
Father Christmas, 1/box
Tomte, 1/kart
H: 2¾". 70 mm

L
97482
Horse, 1/box
Häst, 1/kart
H: 2". 50 mm

M
97858
Trumpet, 1/box
Trumpet, 1/kart
L. 3". 75 mm

N
97695
Christmas pig, 1/box
Julgris, 1/kart
H: 2". 50 mm

O
97745
Heart, 1/box
Hjärta, 1/kart
H: 2". 50 mm

CICERO

DESIGN: ANNA EHRNER. FULL LEAD CRYSTAL, HANDBLOWN. KRISTALL, HANDBLÅST

BOWL. SKÅL
H: 3". 75 MM
Ø: 9". 230 MM
58583 WHITE. VIT
58580 BLUE. BLÅ
58577 BLACK. SVART

BOWL. SKÅL
H: 2". 55 MM
Ø: 5". 130 MM
58581 WHITE. VIT
58578 BLUE. BLÅ
58575 BLACK. SVART

Vase. Vas
H: 8". 200 mm
Ø: 4". 100 mm
48582 White. Vit
48579 Blue. Blå
48576 Black. Svart

Vase. Vas
H: 6½". 165 mm
Ø: 3¼". 85 mm
48581 White. Vit
48578 Blue. Blå
48575 Black. Svart

Bowl. Skål
H: 2¾". 70 mm
Ø: 8". 200 mm
58582 White. Vit
58579 Blue. Blå
58576 Black. Svart

Club

Design: Bertil Vallien. Full Lead Crystal. Kristall

78402
Ashtray, 1/box. Askfat, 1/kart
Ø: 7". 180 mm

78401
Ashtray, 1/box. Askfat, 1/kart
Ø: 6". 150 mm

Cassius

Design: Göran Wärff. Full Lead Crystal. Kristall

78566
Ashtray. Askfat
H: 3¾". 95 mm
Ø: 9½". 240 mm

Not shown:
Visas ej:

78565
Ashtray
Askfat
H: 2¼"
H: 60 mm
Ø: 6½"
Ø: 170 mm

Cross

Design: Monica Backström

78418
Ashtray. Askfat
Ø: 5". 130 mm

78419
Ashtray. Askfat
Ø: 7½". 190 mm

Concorde

Design: Göran Wärff. Full Lead Crystal, Handblown, Cut. Kristall, Handblåst, Slipad

Not shown:
Visas ej:

58567
Bowl. Skål
H: 4¾"
H: 120 mm
Ø: 8½"
Ø: 220 mm

58566
Bowl
Skål
H: 4". 100 mm
Ø: 7". 180 mm

58565
Bowl
Skål
H: 3". 80 mm
Ø: 5". 130 mm

Collage

Design: Anna Ehrner. Full Lead Crystal, Cut. Kristall, Slipad

Candlestick. Ljusstake
2½ × 2½ × 3½". 60 × 60 × 90 mm
68538 Black. Svart
68541 Blue. Blå
68544 White. Vit

CANDLESTICK. LJUSSTAKE
2½ × 2½ × 4½". 60 × 60 × 115 MM
68539 BLACK. SVART
68542 BLUE. BLÅ
68545 WHITE. VIT

CANDLESTICK. LJUSSTAKE
2½ × 2½ × 5½". 60 × 60 × 140 MM
68540 BLACK. SVART
68543 BLUE. BLÅ
68546 WHITE. VIT

Colombine

Design: Anna Ehrner, Handblown. Handblåst

58524
Bowl, 1/box
Skål, 1/kart
H: 6". 150 mm
Ø: 8½". 220 mm

21862
Carafe, 32 oz, 1/box
Karaff, 90 cl, 1/kart
H: 10". 255 mm

58523
Bowl, 1/box
Skål, 1/kart
H: 4½". 115 mm
Ø: 6½". 170 mm

21880
WINE COOLER, 1/BOX
VINKYLARE, 1/KART
H: 8", 200 MM
Ø: 6½", 170 MM

21807
WINE, 9 OZ, 2/BOX
VIN, 25 CL, 2/KART
H: 8½", 215 MM
Ø: 3", 75 MM

21805
WINE, 5¼ OZ, 2/BOX
VIN, 15 CL, 2/KART
H: 7½", 195 MM
Ø: 2¾", 70 MM

21806
WINE, 7 OZ, 2/BOX
VIN, 20 CL, 2/KART
H: 8¼", 210 MM
Ø: 2¾", 70 MM

21801
WINE, 1 OZ, 2/BOX
VIN, 2½ CL, 2/KART
H: 5¼", 135 MM
Ø: 1½", 40 MM

21821
CHAMPAGNE FLUTE, 5¼ OZ, 2/BOX
CHAMPAGNE HÖG, 15 CL, 2/KART
H: 9¼", 235 MM
Ø: 2", 50 MM

21803
WINE, 2½ OZ, 2/BOX
VIN, 7½ CL, 2/KART
H: 6", 150 MM
Ø: 2", 50 MM

21842
TUMBLER, 7 OZ, 2/BOX
TUMBLER, 20 CL, 2/KART
H: 3¼", 85 MM
Ø: 2½", 65 MM

21825
AQUAVIT, 1¾ OZ, 2/BOX
SNAPS, 5 CL, 2/KART
H: 6½", 165 MM
Ø: 2", 50 MM

Colonna

Design: Bengt Edenfalk, Full Lead Crystal. Handblown, Cut. Kristall, Handblåst, Slipad

44270
Vase
Vas
H; 7½", 190 mm

44271
VASE
VAS
H: 6½". 165 MM

44269
VASE
VAS
H: 8½". 220 MM

44268
VASE
VAS
H: 7". 180 MM

CYMBAL

DESIGN: CHRISTIAN VON SYDOW. FULL LEAD CRYSTAL, HANDBLOWN, CUT. KRISTALL, HANDBLÅST, SLIPAD

48568	78561	48566	48562	48564
VASE	ASHTRAY	VASE	VASE	VASE
VAS	ASKFAT	VAS	VAS	VAS
H: 10¼". 265 MM	H: 3¼". 85 MM	H: 13¾". 350 MM	H: 6". 150 MM	H: 10". 250 MM
Ø: 6". 150 MM	Ø: 5¼". 135 MM	Ø: 3". 75 MM	Ø: 1¾". 45 MM	Ø: 2". 50 MM

NOT SHOWN:
VISAS EJ:

48567
VASE. VAS
H: 17″
H: 400 MM
Ø: 3″
Ø: 75 MM

58564
BOWL. SKÅL
H: 3¼″
H: 85 MM
Ø: 7½″
Ø: 195 MM

78562
BOWL
SKÅL
H: 4″. 100 MM
Ø: 9½″. 245 MM

48563
VASE
VAS
H: 8″. 200 MM
Ø: 1¾″. 45 MM

48565
VASE
VAS
H: 11¾″. 300 MM
Ø: 2″. 50 MM

58563
BOWL
SKÅL
H: 3¼″. 75 MM
Ø: 5¼″. 135 MM

58562
BOWL
SKÅL
H: 5″. 130 MM
Ø: 5¼″. 135 MM

Crystal Cube

Design: Göran Wärff. Full Lead Crystal. Kristall

77981
Ashtray
Askfat
Ø: 6 × 6″. 150 × 150 mm

67982
Hurricane, 1/box
Ljuslykta, 1/kart
H: 4″. 100 mm

NOT SHOWN:
VISAS EJ:

77980
ASHTRAY
ASKFAT
Ø: 5 × 5″
Ø: 130 ×
130 MM

97981
LIGHTER, 1/BOX
TÄNDARE, 1/KART
H: 3″. 75 MM

67983
HURRICANE
LJUSLYKTA
H: 6½″. 170 MM

67981
HURRICANE, 1/BOX
LJUSLYKTA, 1/KART
H: 3¼″. 85 MM

Crystal Fantasy

Design: Bertil Vallien. Full Lead Crystal. Kristall

A
98525
Message Over Mountains, 1/box
3¾ × 4 × 3¾″
95 × 100 × 95 mm

B
68531
Candlestick,
Rock of Light, 1/box
2¾ × 2¾ × 3″
70 × 70 × 75 mm

C
68528
Hurricane,
Rock of Light, 1/box
2¾ × 2¾ × 3″
70 × 70 × 75 mm

D
98535
House of Mystery
2½ × 4¼ × 3½″
65 × 110 × 90 mm

E
98526
I'm Gonna Write ..., 1/box
3¾ × 4 × 3¾″
95 × 100 × 95 mm

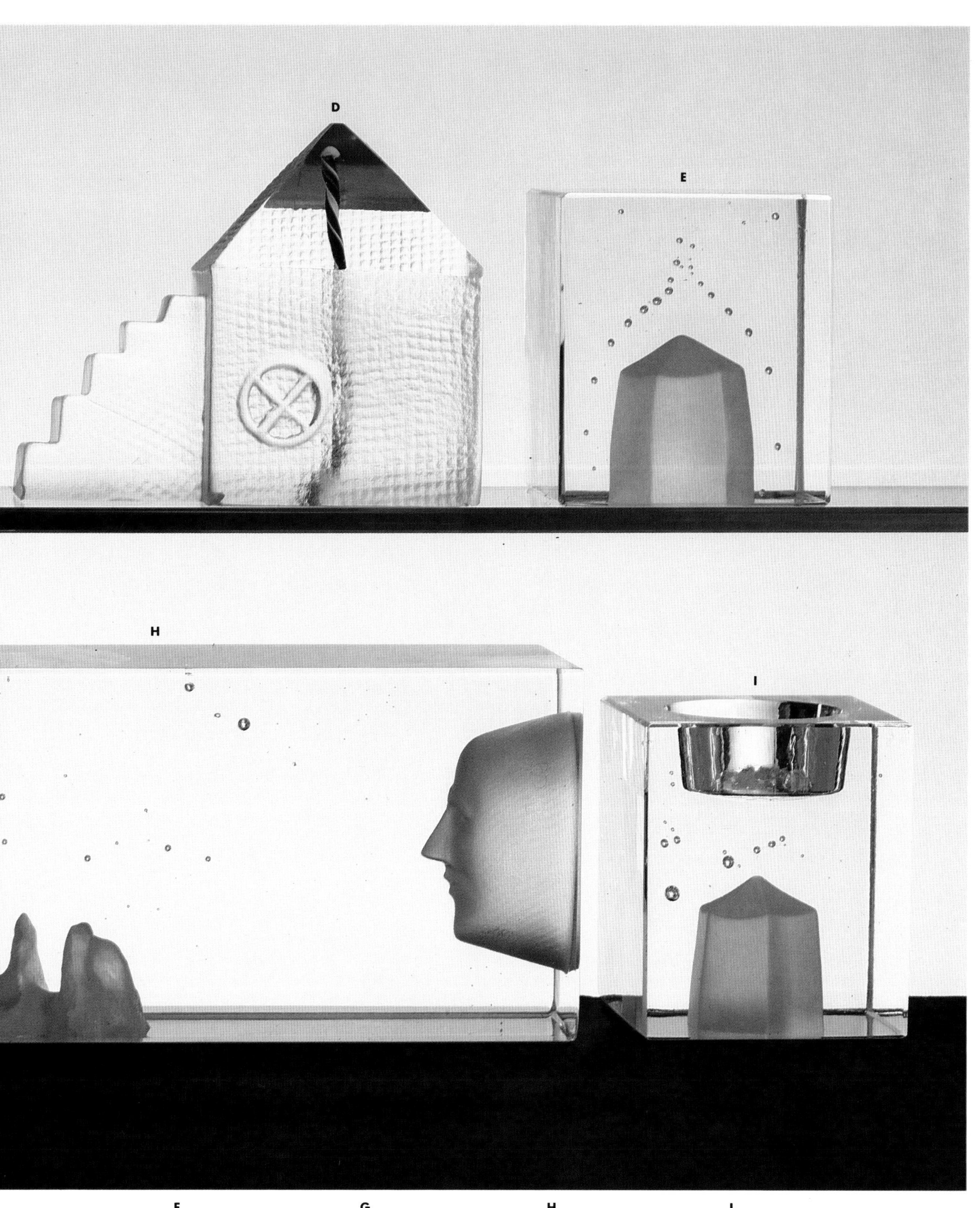

F
68535
HURRICANE
POWER OF REFLECTION
3¾ × 4 × 3¾″
95 × 100 × 95 MM

G
98527
LETTER IN THE SUN, 1/BOX
3¾ × 4 × 3¾″
95 × 100 × 95 MM

H
98549
TIME IS ON MY SIDE
8¼ × 2¾ × 3½″
210 × 70 × 90 MM

I
68530
HURRICANE,
HOUSEWARMING, 1/BOX
2¾ × 2¾ × 3″
70 × 70 × 75 MM

CRYSTAL FANTASY

DESIGN: BERTIL VALLIEN. FULL LEAD CRYSTAL. KRISTALL

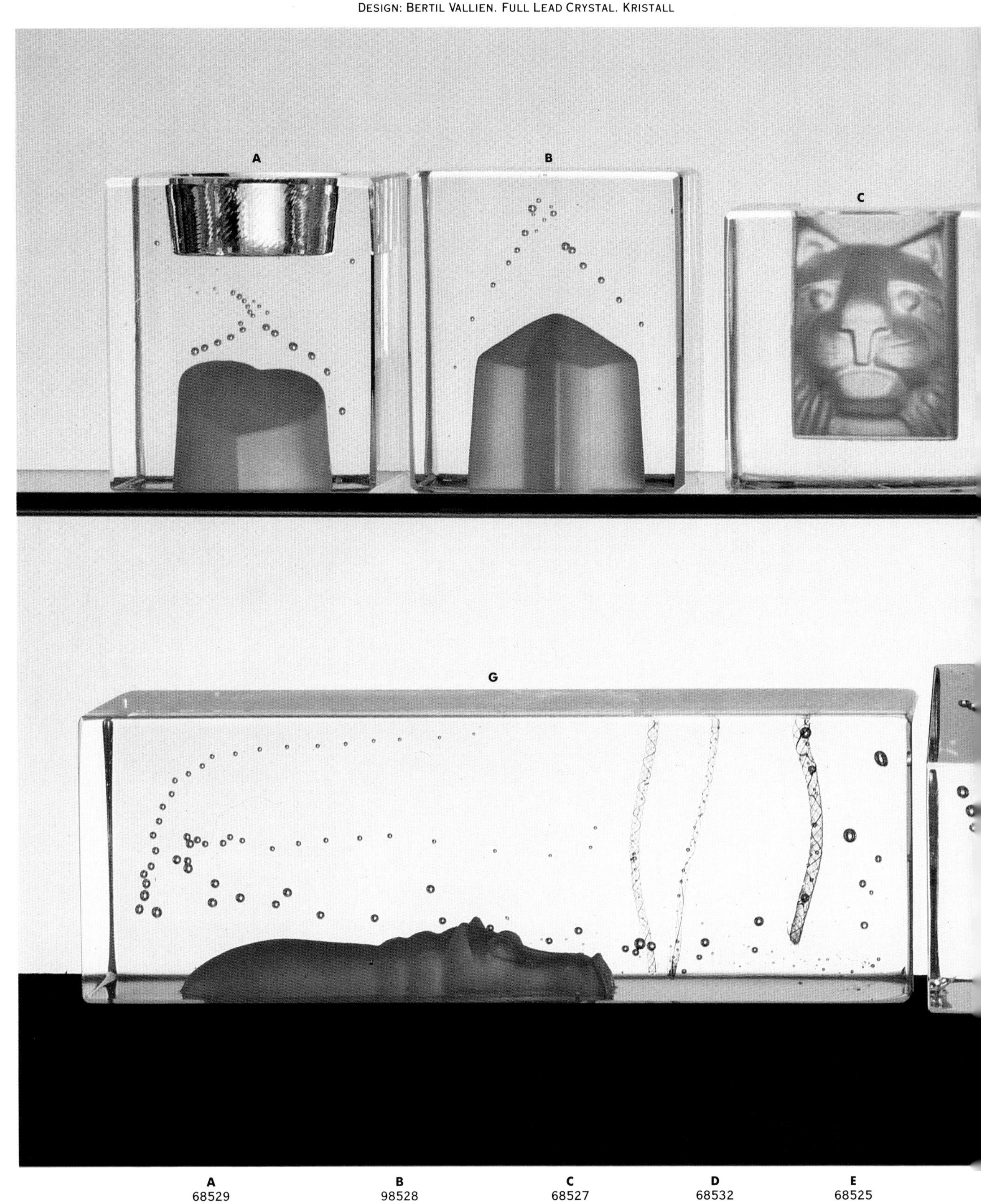

A
68529
HURRICANE,
ENLIGHTENED HEART, 1/BOX
2¾ × 2¾ × 3″
70 × 70 × 75 MM

B
98528
HOMAGE TO A STAR, 1/BOX
3¾ × 4 × 3¾″
95 × 100 × 95 MM

C
68527
HURRICANE,
MAGIC PANTHER, 1/BOX
2¾ × 3 × 2¾″
70 × 75 × 70 MM

D
68532
CANDLESTICK,
HEART, 1/BOX
2¾ × 2¾ × 3″
70 × 70 × 75 MM

E
68525
HURRICANE,
MAGIC FACE, 1/BOX
2¾ × 3 × 2¾″
70 × 75 × 70 MM

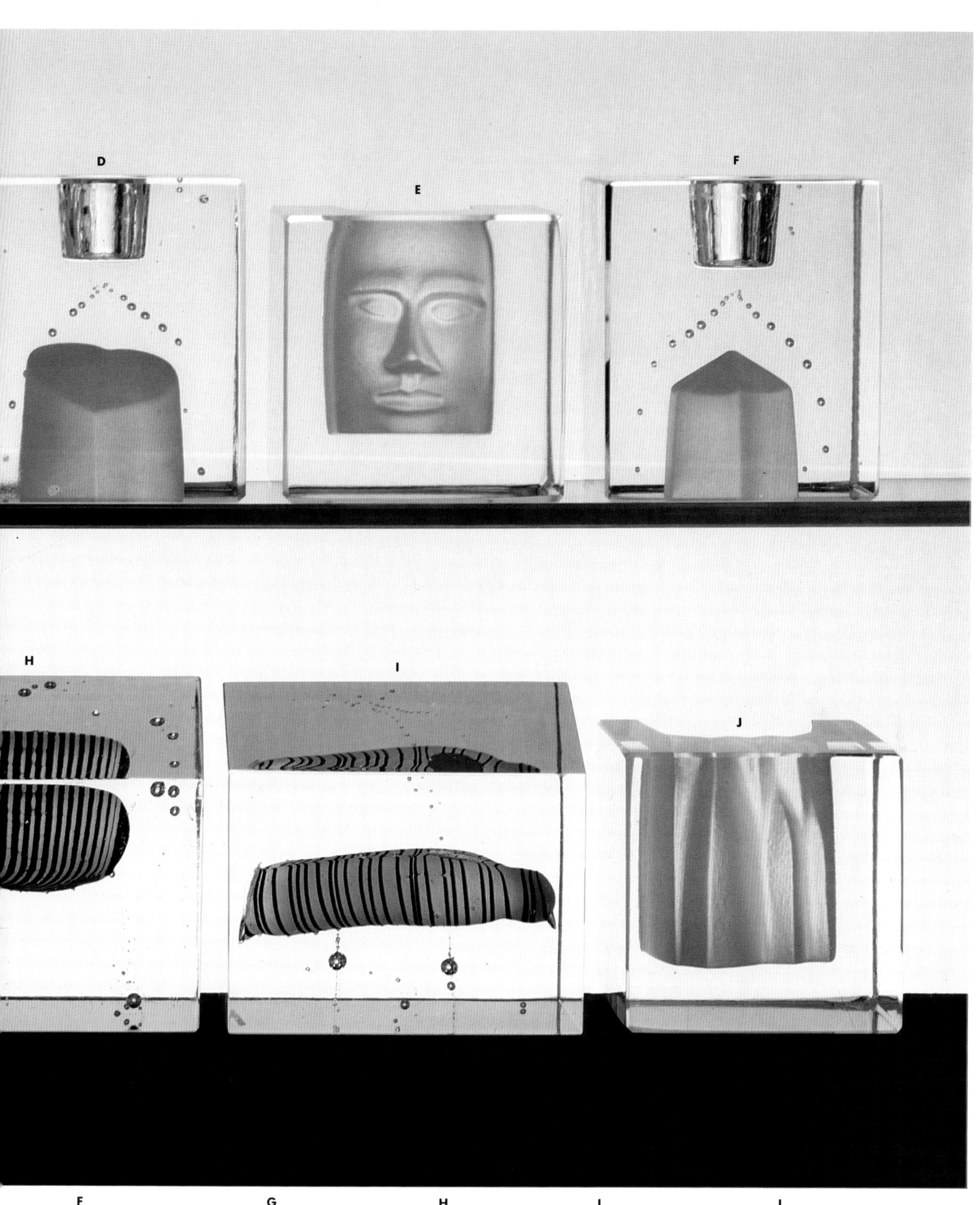

F
68533
CANDLESTICK,
HOUSEWARMING, 1/BOX
2¾ × 2¾ × 3″
70 × 70 × 75 MM

G
98550
DOWN BY THE RIVERSIDE
8¼ × 2¾ × 3½″
210 × 70 × 90 MM

H
98545
THE ASTRONOMER
3¼ × 3¼ × 3″
85 × 85 × 75 MM

I
98546
TRAVELLING MUMMY
3¼ × 3¼ × 3″
85 × 85 × 75 MM

J
68526
HURRICANE,
MAGIC MOUNTAIN, 1/BOX
2¾ × 3 × 2¾″
70 × 75 × 70 MM

Crystal Fantasy

Design: Bertil Vallien. Full Lead Crystal. Kristall

98542
Point of Panther
H: 5¼". 135 mm

98547
Crystal Palace
4 × 4 × 7"
100 × 100 × 180 mm

98541
Point of Black
H: 4¼". 110 mm

98540
Point of Parrot
H: 4¼". 110 mm

98552
STEPS OF LUCK
H: 7½". 190 MM

98536
TENT OF MYSTERY
7½ × 3 × 7¼"
190 × 75 × 185 MM

98538
MUMMY IN TENT
5¾ × 2⅛ × 4½"
145 × 55 × 115 MM

98537
TENT AND BAR
5½ × 2 × 5½"
135 × 55 × 140 MM

Crystal Fantasy

Design: Bertil Vallien. Full Lead Crystal. Kristall

98551
Precious Cargo
15¾ × 4½ × 7½"
390 × 110 × 190 mm

Contra

Design: Göran Wärff
Full Lead Crystal. Kristall

98580
Sculpture
Bordsskulptur
H: 3½". 90 mm
Ø. [illegible] mm

98581
Sculpture with blue line
Bordsskulptur med blå slinga
H: 9½". 240 mm
Ø. [illegible] mm

Dalecarlia

Design: Vicke Lindstrand
Full Lead Crystal, Handblown, Engraved. Kristall, Handblåst, Graverad

96366
Mug, 21 oz
Sejdel, 60 cl
H: 4¾". 120 mm
Ø. [illegible] mm

92394
Wine, 5¼ oz, 1/box
Vin, 15 cl, 1/kart
H: 6¼". 160 mm

Diagonal

Design: Kjell Engman. Full Lead Crystal. Kristall

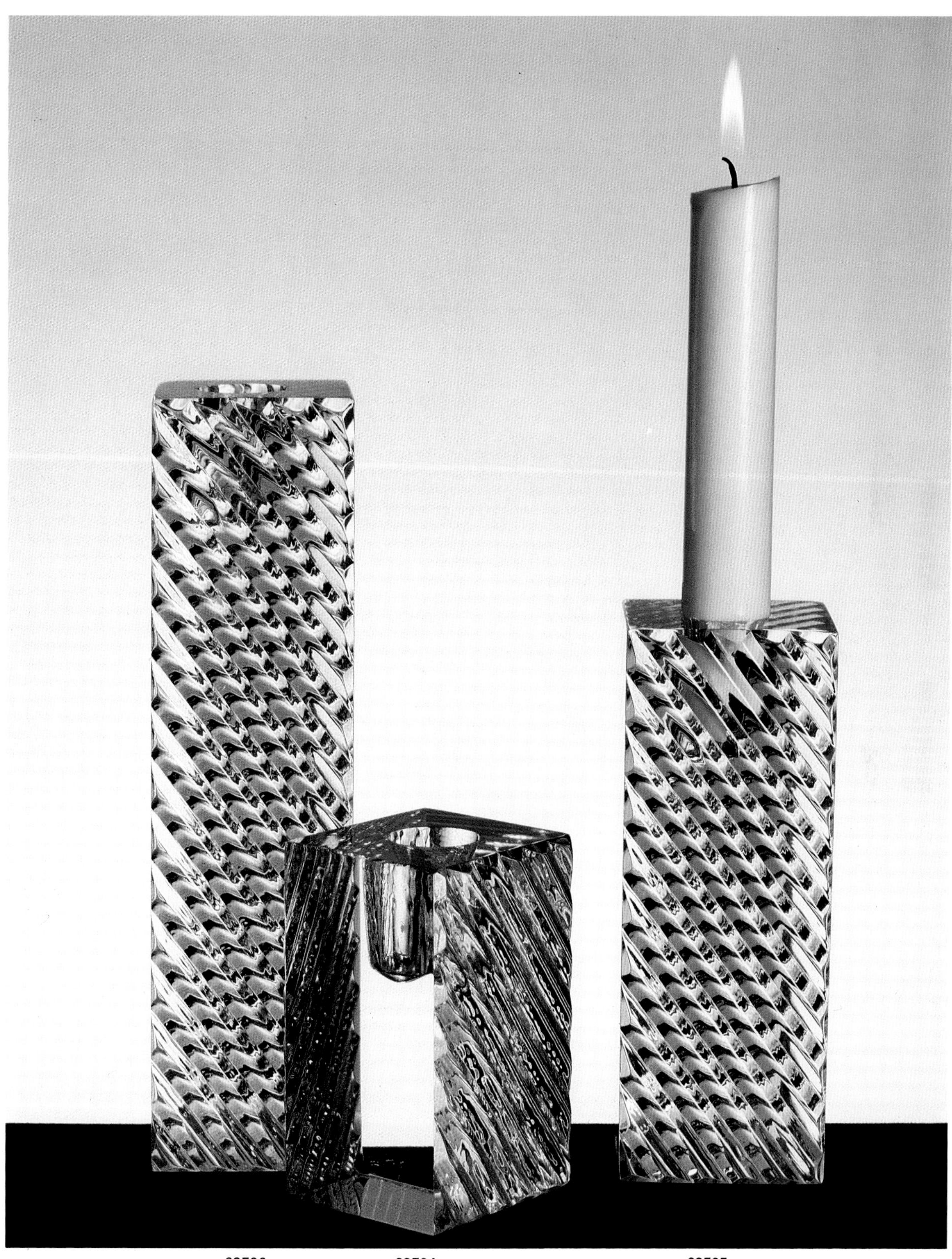

68506	68504	68505
Candlestick, 1/box	Candlestick, 1/box	Candlestick, 1/box
Ljusstake, 1/kart	Ljusstake, 1/kart	Ljusstake, 1/kart
H: 7½". 195 mm	H: 3¾". 95 mm	H: 5¾". 145 mm
Ø: 2". 50 mm	Ø: 2". 50 mm	Ø: 2". 50 mm

Djurgårdsbrunn

Design: Göran Wärff. Full Lead Crystal, Handblown, Cut. Kristall, Handblåst, Slipad

22625
Aquavit, 2 oz
Snaps, 6 cl
H: 6½". 170 mm
Ø: 2". 50 mm

22622
Champagne bowl, 10½ oz
Champagne skål, 30 cl
H: 5½". 140 mm
Ø: 3¾". 95 mm

22662
Decanter, 39 oz
Karaff, 110 cl
H: 10¼". 265 mm

22621
Champagne flute, 5¼ oz
Champagne hög, 15 cl
H: 9½". 240 mm
Ø: 2¼". 60 mm

22606	22663	22603	22608	22649
WINE, 7 OZ	CARAFE, 39 OZ	WINE, 2½ OZ	WINE, 10½ OZ	O F, 7 OZ
VIN, 20 CL	KARAFF, 110 CL	VIN, 7½ CL	VIN, 30 CL	O F, 20 CL
H: 7". 175 MM	H: 12¾". 325 MM	H: 5½". 140 MM	H: 7½". 195 MM	H: 3". 75 MM
Ø: 2¾". 70 MM		Ø: 2¼". 60 MM	Ø: 3". 75 MM	Ø: 3". 75 MM

Engraved Bowls

Design: Lisa Bauer. Full Lead Crystal, Handblown, Engraved. Kristall, Handblåst, Graverad

57993
Bowl, Clover
Skål, Harklöver
H: 5". 130 mm

57994
Bowl, Clover
Skål, Klöver
H: 5". 130 mm

57997
BOWL, ROSE
SKÅL, ROS
H: 5″. 130 MM

57998
BOWL, WILD STRAWBERRIES
SKÅL, SMULTRON
H: 5″. 130 MM

57995
BOWL, BUTTERCUP
SKÅL, SMÖRBLOMMA
H: 5″. 130 MM

EACH PIECE COMES IN ITS OWN WOODEN CASE.
VARJE SKÅL LIGGER I ETT EGET TRÄSCHATULL.

Engraved Vases

Design: Bengt Edenfalk. Full Lead Crystal, Handblown, Engraved. Kristall, Handblåst, Graverad

48070
Vase, Nils Holgersson, rect.
Vas, Nils Holgersson, rekt.
H: 4½". 115 mm

48072
Vase, Swan, hexagonal
Vas, Svan, 6-kt
H: 4½". 115 mm

48073
Vase, Duck, hexagonal
Vas, Anka, 6-kt
H: 4½". 115 mm

48074
VASE, DUCKS, HEXAGONAL
VAS, ANKOR, 6-KT
H: 4¾". 120 MM

48071
VASE, VIKING SHIP, RECT.
VAS, VIKINGASKEPP, REKT.
H: 4½". 115 MM

48075
VASE, SEAGULL, HEXAGONAL
VAS, MÅS, 6-KT
H: 4¾". 120 MM

Feathers

Design: Vicke Lindstrand. Full Lead Crystal, Handblown, Engraved. Kristall, Handblåst, Graverad

52451
Bowl
Skål
H: 8¼". 210 mm
Ø: 8". 200 mm

FLUTE

DESIGN: ROLF SINNEMARK. HANDBLOWN. HANDBLÅST

48319	48318
VASE, 1/BOX	VASE, 1/BOX
VAS, 1/KART	VAS, 1/KART
H: 8¼". 210 MM	H: 6¼". 160 MM

FLOWER

DESIGN: BERTIL VALLIEN. HANDBLOWN. HANDBLÅST

47701
VASE, 1/BOX
VAS, 1/KART
H: 4½". 115 MM

47703
VASE, 1/BOX
VAS, 1/KART
H: 7½". 190 MM

47700
Vase, 1/box
Vas, 1/kart
H: 2¾". 70 mm

47706
Vase
Vas
H: 6¼". 160 mm

47705
Vase
Vas
H: 5". 130 mm

47702
Vase, 1/box
Vas, 1/kart
H: 6". 150 mm

Focus

Design: Christian von Sydow. Handblown. Handblåst

Decanter. Karaff	98603 Black. Svart
21 oz, 1/box. 60 cl, 1/kart	98604 Yellow. Gul
H: 9½". 240 mm	98605 Red. Röd

Cocktail
2 oz, 1/box. 6 cl, 1/kart
H: 2¼". 60 mm Ø: 2¾". 70 mm

98650 Black. Svart
98651 Red. Röd
98652 Yellow. Gul
98653 Violet. Violett
98654 Blue. Blå
98655 Green. Grön

Cocktail
5¼ oz, 1/box. 15 cl, 1/kart
H: 3". 75 mm Ø: 3¾". 95 mm

98656 Black. Svart
98657 Red. Röd
98658 Yellow. Gul
98659 Violet. Violett
98660 Blue. Blå
98661 Green. Grön

Fragancia

Design: Göran Wärff. Full Lead Crystal, Handblown. Kristall, Handblåst

Bowl. Skål
Ø: 12". 305 mm
58352 Blue. Blå
58355 Red. Röd

VASE. VAS
H: 6½". 165 MM
48353 RED. RÖD
48350 BLUE. BLÅ

BOWL. SKÅL
Ø: 7". 175 MM
58350 BLUE. BLÅ
58353 RED. RÖD

BOWL. SKÅL
Ø: 8½". 215 MM
58351 BLUE. BLÅ
58354 RED. RÖD

Frost

Design: Rolf Sinnemark. Handblown. Handblåst

98322
Aquavit, 1 oz, 2/box
Snaps, 2½ cl, 2/kart
H: 7½". 195 mm
Ø: 1½". 35 mm

88320
Decanter, 26 oz, 1/box
Karaff, 75 cl, 1/kart
H: 8". 200 mm

78322
Ashtray, 1/box
Askfat, 1/kart
Ø: 6". 150 mm

98324
Martini, 4¾ oz, 2/box
Martini, 13 cl, 2/kart
H: 4¾". 120 mm
Ø: 4½". 115 mm

78320
Ashtray, 1/box
Askfat, 1/kart
Ø: 3 × 3". 75 × 75 mm

NOT SHOWN:
VISAS EJ:

22349
O F, 7 OZ,
2/BOX
O F, 20 CL,
2/KART
H: 3¼". 85 MM
Ø: 3". 75 MM

22334
MARTINI,
5¼ OZ
MARTINI,
15 CL
H: 6½"
H: 165 MM

22335
MARTINI,
5¼ OZ
MARTINI,
15 CL
H: 6½"
H: 165 MM

88521
DECANTER, 30 OZ, 1/BOX
KARAFF, 85 CL, 1/KART
H: 11¾". 300 MM

88321
DECANTER, 19½ OZ, 1/BOX
KARAFF, 55 CL, 1/KART
H: 9". 225 MM

88322
DECANTER, 26½ OZ, 1/BOX
KARAFF, 75 CL, 1/KART
H: 11". 275 MM

22348
HIGHBALL, 14 OZ, 2/BOX
GROGGLAS, 40 CL, 2/KART
H: 6¼". 160 MM
Ø: 2¾". 70 MM

22350
D O F, 9 OZ, 2/BOX
D O F, 25 CL, 2/KART
H: 4". 100 MM
Ø: 3¼". 85 MM

FROST

DESIGN: ROLF SINNEMARK. HANDBLOWN. HANDBLÅST

58322
BOWL, 1/BOX
SKÅL, 1/KART
6 × 6". 155 × 155 MM

98320
ICE BUCKET, 1/BOX
ISHINK, 1/KART
6¼ x 6¼". 160 x 160 MM

68520
CANDLESTICK, 1/BOX
LJUSSTAKE, 1/KART
H: 4½". 115 MM
Ø: 2". 50 MM

68522
CANDLESTICK, 1/BOX
LJUSSTAKE, 1/KART
H: 8¼". 210 MM
Ø: 2". 50 MM

68521
CANDLESTICK, 1/BOX
LJUSSTAKE, 1/KART
H: 6". 150 MM
Ø: 2". 50 MM

58441
BOWL, 1/BOX
SKÅL, 1/KART
Ø: 10¼". 265 MM

78321
ASHTRAY, 1/BOX
ASKFAT, 1/KART
Ø: 5 × 5". 130 × 130 MM

GRACE

DESIGN: KOSTA BODA TRADITIONAL. HANDBLOWN. HANDBLÅST

44065
VASE, 1/BOX
VAS, 1/KART
H: 11¼". 290 MM

GRAND

DESIGN: ANNA EHRNER. FULL LEAD CRYSTAL, HANDBLOWN, CUT. KRISTALL, HANDBLÅST, SLIPAD

NOT SHOWN:
VISAS EJ:

48307
VASE. VAS
H: 6¼"
H: 160 MM

48308
VASE
VAS
H: 8". 200 MM

Grape

Design: Ann Wärff

97554
Beer/wine, 10¼ oz, 2/box
Öl/vin, 30 cl, 2/kart
H: 5¾", 145 mm
Ø: 2¾", 70 mm

57618
Dessert bowl, 2/box
Dessertskål, 2/kart
Ø: 5¼", 135 mm

57556
Bowl, 1/box
Skål, 1/kart
Ø: 9", 225 mm

NOT SHOWN:
VISAS EJ:

57619
DESSERT BOWL, 1/BOX
DESSERT-SKÅL, 1/KART
Ø: 6½″
Ø: 170 MM

57620
FRUIT BOWL, 1/BOX
FRUKTSKÅL, 1/KART
Ø: 10″
Ø: 250 MM

57554
BOWL, 1/BOX
SKÅL, 1/KART
Ø: 4¼″. 115 MM

57555
BOWL, 1/BOX
SKÅL, 1/KART
Ø: 7¼″. 185 MM

GRAPE

DESIGN: ANN WÄRFF

97159
SMALL PLATTER, 2/BOX
SMÖRGÅSASSIETT, 2/KART
Ø: 8½". 220 MM

97160
CHEESE PLATE, 1/BOX
OSTBRICKA, 1/KART
Ø: 12½". 320 MM

77161
FRUIT DISH, 1/BOX
FRUKTFAT, 1/KART
Ø: 13¼". 340 MM

Not shown:
Visas ej:

77760
Fruit dish,
1/box
Fruktfat,
1/kart
Ø: 10½"
Ø: 270 mm

77806
Cheese plate
Ostbricka
Ø: 10¼"
Ø: 260 mm

97161
Cheese plate,
1/box
Ostbricka,
1/kart
Ø: 15"
Ø: 380 mm

77160
Plate, 2/box
Tallrik, 2/kart
Ø: 10". 255 mm

77805
Cheese plate, 1/box
Ostbricka, 1/kart
Ø: 12½". 320 mm

77159
Small plate, 2/box
Assiett, 2/kart
Ø: 7". 180 mm

Harebell

Design: Sigurd Persson/Lisa Bauer. Full Lead Crystal, Handblown, Engraved. Kristall, Handblåst, Graverad

57094	57096
Bowl, 1/box	Bowl
Skål, 1/kart	Skål
H; 6″, 150 mm	H: 4¾″, 120 mm
Ø: 6″. 150 mm	Ø: 3¾″. 95 mm

Harlequin

Design: Ann Wärff. Full Lead Crystal, Handblown, Cut. Kristall, Handblåst, Slipad

57366
Bowl. Skål
Ø: 6½". 170 mm

Heart

Design: Bertil Vallien. Handblown. Handblåst

47602	47613
Vase, 1/box	Miniature vase, 12/box
Vas, 1/kart	Miniatyrvas, 12/kart
H: 4". 100 mm	H: 3¼". 85 mm

HOLLYWOOD

DESIGN: MONICA BACKSTRÖM. HANDBLOWN. HANDBLÅST

48621
VASE, 1/BOX
VAS, 1/KART
H: 8[illegible]", 220 MM

48619
VASE, 1/BOX
VAS, 1/KART
H: 7". 180 MM

48620
VASE, 1/BOX
VAS, 1/KART
H: 7". 180 MM

Hollywood White

Design: Monica Backström. Handblown. Handblåst

48624
Vase, 1/box
Vas, 1/kart
H: 8¼", 220 MM

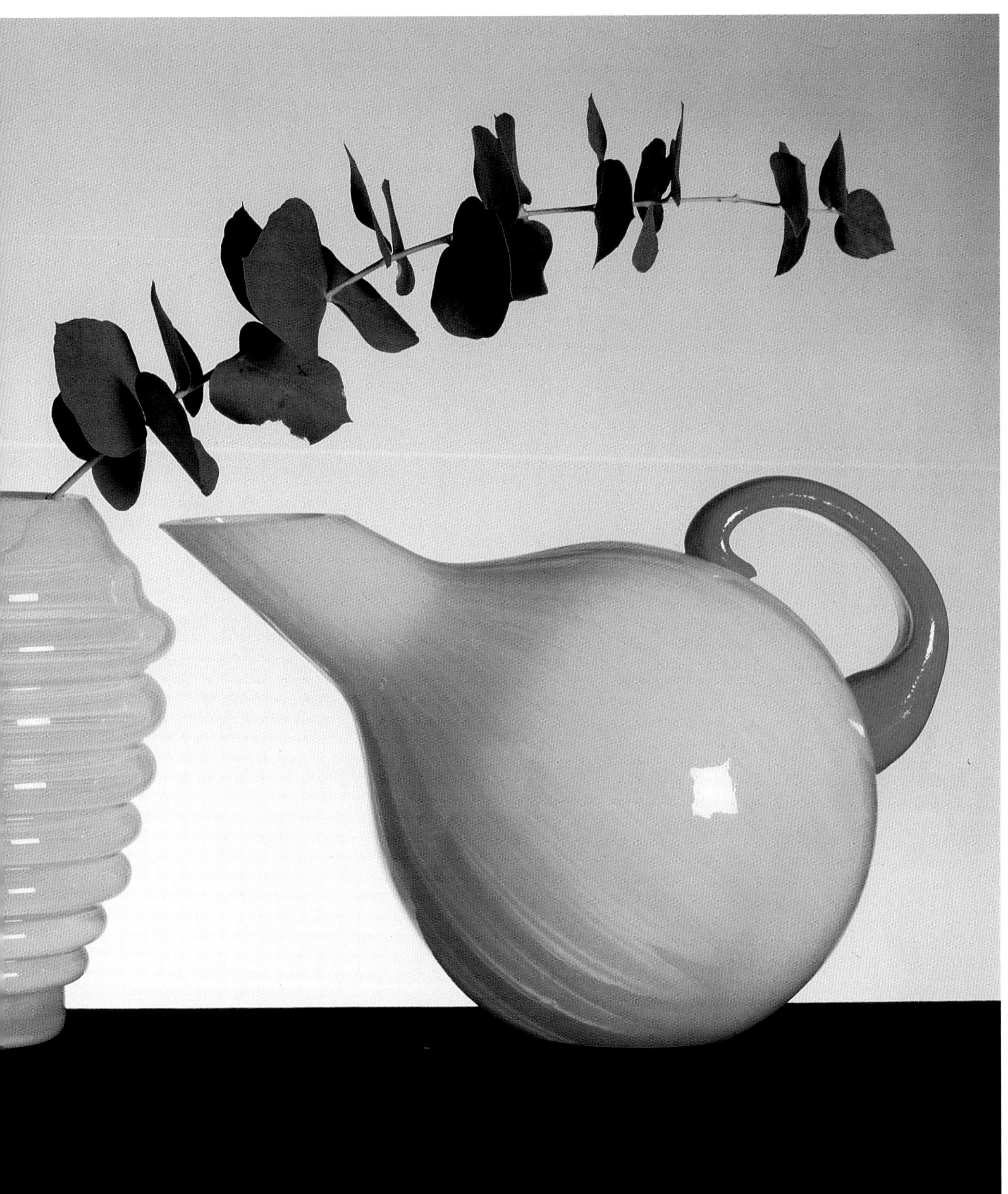

NOT SHOWN:
VISAS EJ:

48623
VASE, 1/BOX
VAS, 1/KART
H: 7″
H: 180 MM

88601
JUG, YELLOW
42 OZ, 1/BOX
KANNA, GUL
120 CL, 1/KART
H: 7¼″
H: 185 MM

48622
VASE, 1/BOX
VAS, 1/KART
H: 7″. 180 MM

88602
JUG, BLUE, 42 OZ, 1/BOX
KANNA, BLÅ, 120 CL, 1/KART
H: 7¼″. 185 MM

ICEBERGS

DESIGN: MATS JONASSON. FULL LEAD CRYSTAL. KRISTALL

93155
WALRUSES, 1/BOX
VALROSSAR, 1/KART
H: 6¼". 160 MM
L: 10". 250 MM

93153
POLAR BEARS, 1/BOX
ISBJÖRNAR, 1/KART
H: 5". 130 MM
L: 8". 200 MM

93190
VIKING SHIP, 1/BOX
VIKINGASKEPP, 1/KART
H: 5½". 140 MM
L: 9½". 240 MM

Icebergs

Design: Vicke Lindstrand. Engraved. Graverad

90078
Sailboat
Segelbåt
L: 6½". 170 mm
H: 7½". 190 mm

NOT SHOWN:
VISAS EJ:

90011
WANDERING POLAR BEARS.
VANDRANDE ISBJÖRNAR.
L: 7½"
L: 190 MM
H: 4¾"
H: 120 MM

90019
POLAR BEAR, DOUBLE SIDED.
ISBJÖRN, DUBBELSIDIG.
L: 11"
L: 280 MM
H: 9½"
H: 245 MM

90042
SWIMMING POLAR BEAR AND FAMILY
SIMMANDE ISBJÖRN OCH FAMILJ
L: 11¼". 285 MM
H: 9¼". 235 MM

90012
WANDERING POLAR BEARS
VANDRANDE ISBJÖRNAR
L: 10". 250 MM
H: 5¾". 145 MM

90013
WANDERING POLAR BEARS
VANDRANDE ISBJÖRNAR
L: 11¼". 285 MM
H:6½". 170 MM

90001
REINDEER
REN
L: 4". 100 MM
H: 4¼". 110 MM

90006
LAPLANDER AND REINDEER
LAPP OCH REN
L: 9½". 245 MM
H: 6". 150 MM

90016
SWIMMING POLAR BEAR
SIMMANDE ISBJÖRN
L: 9". 225 MM
H: 7". 175 MM

97676
VIKING SHIP
VIKINGASKEPP
L: 7½". 190 MM
H: 5". 125 MM

IMPRESSIONS

DESIGN: BENGT EDENFALK. HANDBLOWN, FULL LEAD CRYSTAL. HANDBLÅST, KRISTALL

48626
VASE
VAS
H: 9". 225 MM

48625
VASE
VAS
H: 7¼". 185 MM

58626
BOWL
SKÅL
H: 5". 125 MM
Ø: 6¼". 160 MM

58625
BOWL
SKÅL
H: 4". 100 MM
Ø: 5". 125 MM

48627
VASE
VAS
H: 11¼". 290 MM

58627
BOWL
SKÅL
H: 6". 150 MM
Ø: 7½". 195 MM

JENNY

DESIGN: BERTIL VALLIEN. HANDBLOWN. HANDBLÅST

47959
VASE, 1/BOX
VAS, 1/KART
H: 5". 130 MM

48140
BUD VASE, 1/BOX
ORKIDÉVAS, 1/KART
H: 9". 225 MM

47960
VASE, 1/BOX
VAS, 1/KART
H: 8". 200 MM

47961
VASE, 1/BOX
VAS, 1/KART
H: 5¼". 135 MM

Karlberg

Design: Elis Bergh. Full Lead Crystal, Handblown, Cut. Kristall, Handblåst, Slipad

90088	22507	22523	22505	22525
Tumbler, 5¼ oz	Wine, 9 oz	Madeira bowl, 2 oz	Wine, 5¼ oz	Aquavit, 1 oz
Tumbler, 15 cl	Vin, 25 cl	Madeiraskål, 6 cl	Vin, 15 cl	Snaps, 2½ cl
H: 3". 75 mm	H: 5¼". 135 mm	H: 3". 75 mm	H: 4½". 115 mm	H: 3¾". 95 mm
Ø: 2¼". 60 mm	Ø: 3". 75 mm	Ø: 2½". 65 mm	Ø: 2¾". 70 mm	Ø: 1¾". 45 mm

22521
CHAMPAGNE FLUTE, 3½ OZ
CHAMPAGNE HÖG, 10 CL
H: 6¼". 160 MM
Ø: 2". 50 MM

22542
TUMBLER, 5¼ OZ
TUMBLER, 15 CL
H: 3". 75 MM
Ø: 2". 50 MM

22506
WINE, 7 OZ
VIN, 20 CL
H: 5¼". 130 MM
Ø: 2¾". 70 MM

22501
WINE, 1 OZ
VIN, 2½ CL
H: 3¼". 85 MM
Ø: 1¼". 35 MM

22503
WINE, 2½ OZ
VIN, 7½ CL
H: 3¾". 95 MM
Ø: 2". 50 MM

Lamps

Design: Monica Backström. Handblown. Handblåst

97947
Pink Mushroom
Rosa Svamp
H; 7", 180 mm

97915
Spotted Mushroom
Snöbollchampignon
H: 10¼", 260 mm

Not shown:
Visas ej:

97809
Agaric
Vax-
skivling
H: 10¼"
H: 260 mm

98023
Cep Brown
Brun Karl-
Johan
H: 6"
H: 150 mm

97803
Agaric
Vaxskivling
H: 7¼". 185 mm

97804
Cep Brown
Brun Karl-Johan
H: 10¼". 260 mm

Lamps

Design: Bertil Vallien

98172	98181
Volcano (no lampshade)	Lampshade, white
Volcano (utan skärm)	Skärm, vit
H: 18". 450 mm	H: 8½". 220 mm

Lamps

Design: Bertil Vallien

Galaxy (no lampshade. utan skärm)
H: 18". 450 mm
98166 Red/White. Röd/Vit
98168 Blue/White. Blå/Vit
98170 Red/Black. Röd/Svart

LIMELIGHT

DESIGN: GÖRAN WÄRFF. FULL LEAD CRYSTAL. KRISTALL

58530
BOWL, 1/BOX
SKÅL, 1/KART
H: 1¾". 45 MM
Ø: 6½". 165 MM

78533
SERVING PLATE, 1/BOX
FAT, 1/KART
Ø: 12½". 320 MM

78531
PLATE, 2/BOX
TALLRIK, 2/KART
Ø: 10¼". 260 MM

Not shown:
Visas ej:

58631
Bowl, 1/box
Skål, 1/kart
H: 4″
H: 105 mm
Ø: 11¾″
Ø: 300 mm

78633
Serving plate,
1/box
Fat, 1/kart
Ø: 13¼″
Ø: 340 mm

78634
Fondue
plate, 2/box
Fondue
tallrik, 2/kart
Ø: 11¾″
Ø: 300 mm

78530
Small plate, 2/box
Assiett, 2/kart
Ø: 8″. 200 mm

78532
Oyster plate, 2/box
Ostrontallrik, 2/kart
Ø: 11″. 280 mm

58531
Bowl, 1/box
Skål, 1/kart
H: 3¼″. 85 mm
Ø: 10¼″. 265 mm

Line

Design: Anna Ehrner. Handblown. Handblåst

21505	21507	98205	21501	21562	21506
Wine, 5¼ oz, 2/box	Wine, 9 oz, 2/box	Wine glass with green line	Wine, 1¼ oz, 2/box	Carafe, 28 oz, 1/box	Wine, 7 oz, 2/box
Vin, 15 cl, 2/kart	Vin, 25 cl, 2/kart	5¼ oz, 2/box	Vin, 3½ cl, 2/kart	Karaff, 80 cl, 1/kart	Vin, 20 cl, 2/kart
H: 8". 205 mm	H: 9". 230 mm	Vinglas med grön slinga	H: 5½". 140 mm	H: 11". 280 mm	H: 8½". 220 mm
Ø: 2¾". 70 mm	Ø: 3". 75 mm	15 cl, 2/kart	Ø: 1¾". 45 mm		Ø: 2¾". 70 mm
		H: 8". 205 mm Ø: 2¾". 70 mm			

21580
Wine cooler, 1/box
Vinkylare, 1/kart
H: 8″. 200 mm
Ø: 7″. 170 mm

21521
Champagne flute, 6¼ oz, 2/box
Champagne hög, 18 cl, 2/kart
H: 10″. 255 mm
Ø: 2¼″. 55 mm

21503
Wine, 2½ oz, 2/box
Vin, 7½ cl, 2/kart
H: 6½″. 165 mm
Ø: 2″. 50 mm

LINE

DESIGN: ANNA EHRNER. HANDBLOWN. HANDBLÅST

21590
HIGHBALL, 14 OZ, 2/BOX
GROGGLAS, 40 CL, 2/KART
H: 6". 150 MM
Ø: 2½". 65 MM

21531
COGNAC, 9 OZ, 2/BOX
COGNAC, 25 CL, 2/KART
H: 4½". 115 MM

21581
ICE BUCKET, 35 OZ, 1/BOX
ISHINK, 100 CL, 1/KART
H: 5". 130 MM
Ø: 6". 150 MM

21525
AQUAVIT, 2 OZ, 2/BOX
SNAPS, 5 CL, 2/KART
H: 6". 150 MM
Ø: 2". 50 MM

21591	88227	21589	21533	21588
Cocktail, 6¼ oz, 2/box	Jug, 52 oz	D O F, 14 oz, 2/box	Martini, 5¼ oz, 2/box	O F, 10½ oz, 2/box
Cocktail, 18 cl, 2/kart	Kanna, 150 cl	D O F, 40 cl, 2/kart	Martini, 15 cl, 2/kart	O F, 30 cl, 2/kart
H: 3". 75 mm	H: 9". 225 mm	H: 4". 100 mm	H: 6½". 165 mm	H: 3¾". 95 mm
Ø: 2½". 65 mm		Ø: 3¼". 85 mm	Ø: 4¼". 110 mm	Ø: 3". 75 mm

LINE

DESIGN: ANNA EHRNER. HANDBLOWN. HANDBLÅST

68317	68316	48248	48247
CANDLESTICK, 1/BOX	CANDLESTICK, 1/BOX	VASE, 1/BOX	VASE, 1/BOX
LJUSSTAKE, 1/KART	LJUSSTAKE, 1/KART	VAS, 1/KART	VAS, 1/KART
Ø: 5". 125 MM	Ø: 4¼". 110 MM	H: 10". 250 MM	H: 7½". 190 MM

68315
CANDLESTICK, 1/BOX
LJUSSTAKE, 1/KART
Ø: 3¾". 95 MM

58228
BOWL, 1/BOX
SKÅL, 1/KART
Ø: 7½". 195 MM

58227
BOWL, 1/BOX
SKÅL, 1/KART
Ø: 6¼". 160 MM

Line Black

Design: Anna Ehrner. Handblown. Handblåst

21633	21687	21606	21625	21605	21601
Martini, 5¼ oz, 2/box	Cocktail, 6¼ oz, 2/box	Wine, 7 oz, 2/box	Aquavit, 2 oz, 2/box	Wine, 5¼ oz, 2/box	Wine, 1¼ oz, 2/box
Martini, 15 cl, 2/kart	Cocktail, 18 cl, 2/kart	Vin, 20 cl, 2/kart	Snaps, 5 cl, 2/kart	Vin, 15 cl, 2/kart	Vin, 3½ cl, 2/kart
H: 6½". 165 mm	H: 3". 75 mm	H: 8½". 220 mm	H: 6". 150 mm	H: 8". 200 mm	H: 5½". 140 mm
Ø: 4¼". 110 mm	Ø: 2½". 65 mm	Ø: 2¾". 70 mm	Ø: 2". 50 mm	Ø: 2¾". 70 mm	Ø: 1¾". 45 mm

21621	21603	68321	68322	21607	68323
CHAMPAGNE FLUTE, 6¼ OZ, 2/BOX	WINE, 2½ OZ, 2/BOX	CANDLESTICK, 1/BOX	CANDLESTICK, 1/BOX	WINE, 9 OZ, 2/BOX	CANDLESTICK, 1/BOX
CHAMPAGNE HÖG, 18 CL, 2/KART	VIN, 7½ CL, 2/KART	LJUSSTAKE, 1/KART	LJUSSTAKE, 1/KART	VIN, 25 CL, 2/KART	LJUSSTAKE, 1/KART
H: 10". 255 MM	H: 6½". 165 MM	Ø: 3¾". 95 MM	Ø: 4¼". 110 MM	H; 9". 230 MM	Ø: 5". 125 MM
Ø: 2¼". 60 MM	Ø: 2". 50 MM			Ø: 3". 75 MM	

LINE GOLD

DESIGN: ANNA EHRNER. HANDBLOWN. HANDBLÅST

21703	21788	21707	21790	21731
WINE, 2½ OZ, 2/BOX	O F, 10½ OZ, 2/BOX	WINE, 9 OZ, 2/BOX	HIGHBALL, 14 OZ, 2/BOX	COGNAC, 9 OZ, 2/BOX
VIN, 7½ CL, 2/KART	O F, 30 CL, 2/KART	VIN, 25 CL, 2/KART	GROGGLASS, 40 CL, 2/KART	COGNAC, 25 CL, 2/KART
H: 6½". 165 MM	H: 3¾". 95 MM	H: 9", 230 MM	H: 6". 150 MM	H: 4½". 115 MM
Ø: 2". 50 MM	Ø: 3". 75 MM	Ø: 3". 75 MM	Ø: 2½". 65 MM	

Not shown:
Visas ej:

21705
Wine, 5¼ oz, 2/box
Vin, 15 cl, 2/kart
H: 8″
H: 200 mm
Ø: 2¾″
Ø: 70 mm

21780
Wine cooler, 1/box
Vinkylare, 1/kart
H: 8″
H: 200 mm
W: 7″
W: 170 mm

21789
D O F, 14 oz, 2/box
D O F, 40 cl, 2/kart
H: 4″
H: 100 mm
Ø: 3¼″
Ø: 85 mm

21706
Wine, 7 oz, 2/box
Vin, 20 cl, 2/kart
H: 8½″. 220 mm
Ø: 2¾″. 70 mm

21725
Aquavit, 2 oz, 2/box
Snaps, 5 cl, 2/kart
H: 6″. 150 mm
Ø: 2″. 50 mm

21721
Champagne flute, 6¼ oz, 2/box
Champagne hög, 18 cl, 2/kart
H: 10″. 255 mm
Ø: 2¼″. 60 mm

21791
Cocktail glass, 6¼ oz, 2/box
Cocktailglas, 18 cl, 2/kart
H: 3″. 75 mm
Ø: 2½″. 65 mm

21733
Martini, 5¼ oz, 2/box
Martini, 15 cl, 2/kart
H: 6½″. 165 mm
Ø: 4¼″. 110 mm

21701
Wine, 1¼ oz, 2/box
Vin, 3½ cl, 2/kart
H: 5½″. 140 mm
Ø: 1¾″. 45 mm

Maxim

Design: Anna Ehrner

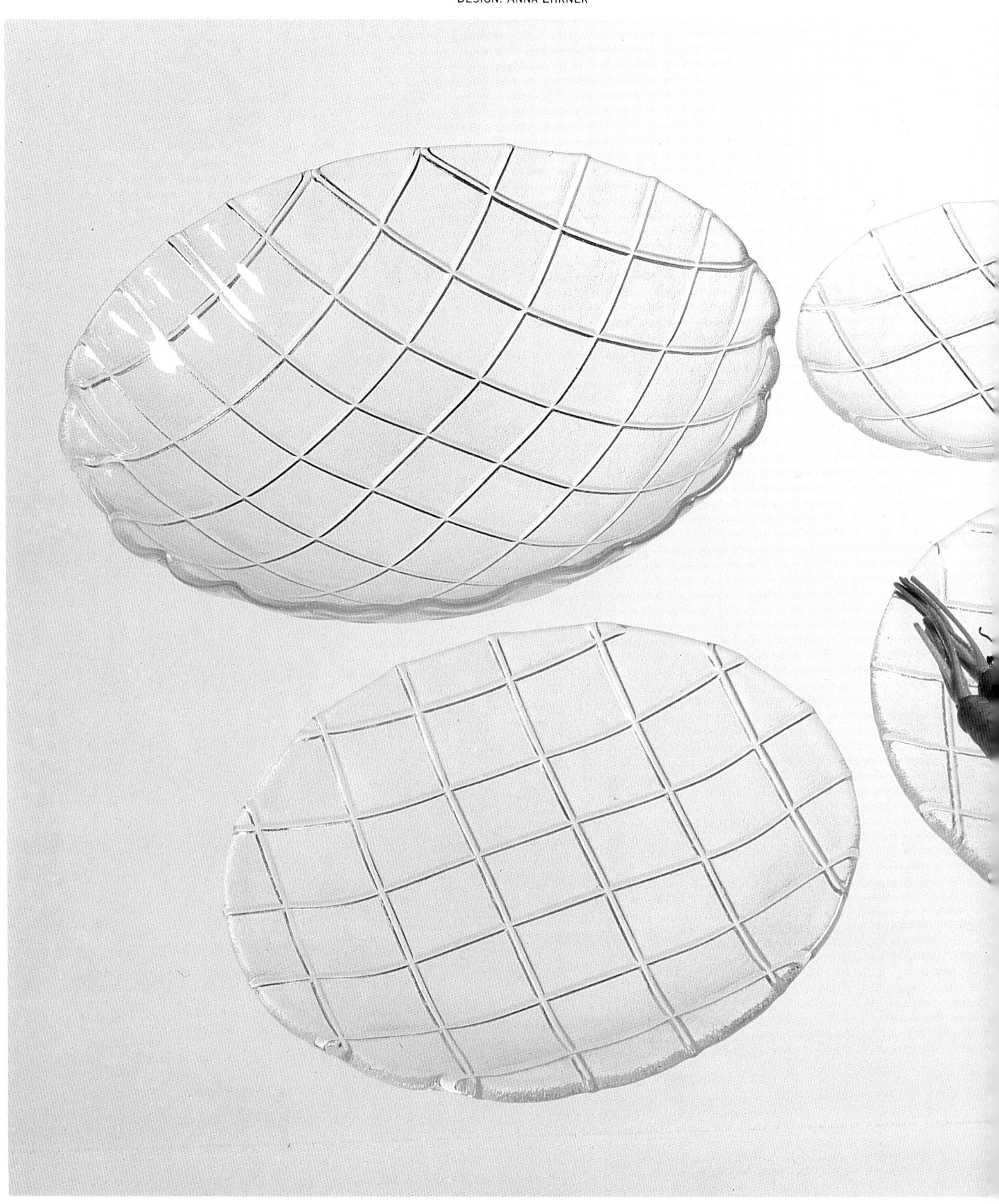

78427
Deep dish, 1/box
Skålfat, 1/kart
Ø: 12¼". 310 mm

78426
Dinner plate, 2/box
Mattallrik, 2/kart
Ø: 10¼". 260 mm

78425
Plate, 2/box
Assiett, 2/kart
Ø: 7½". 190 mm

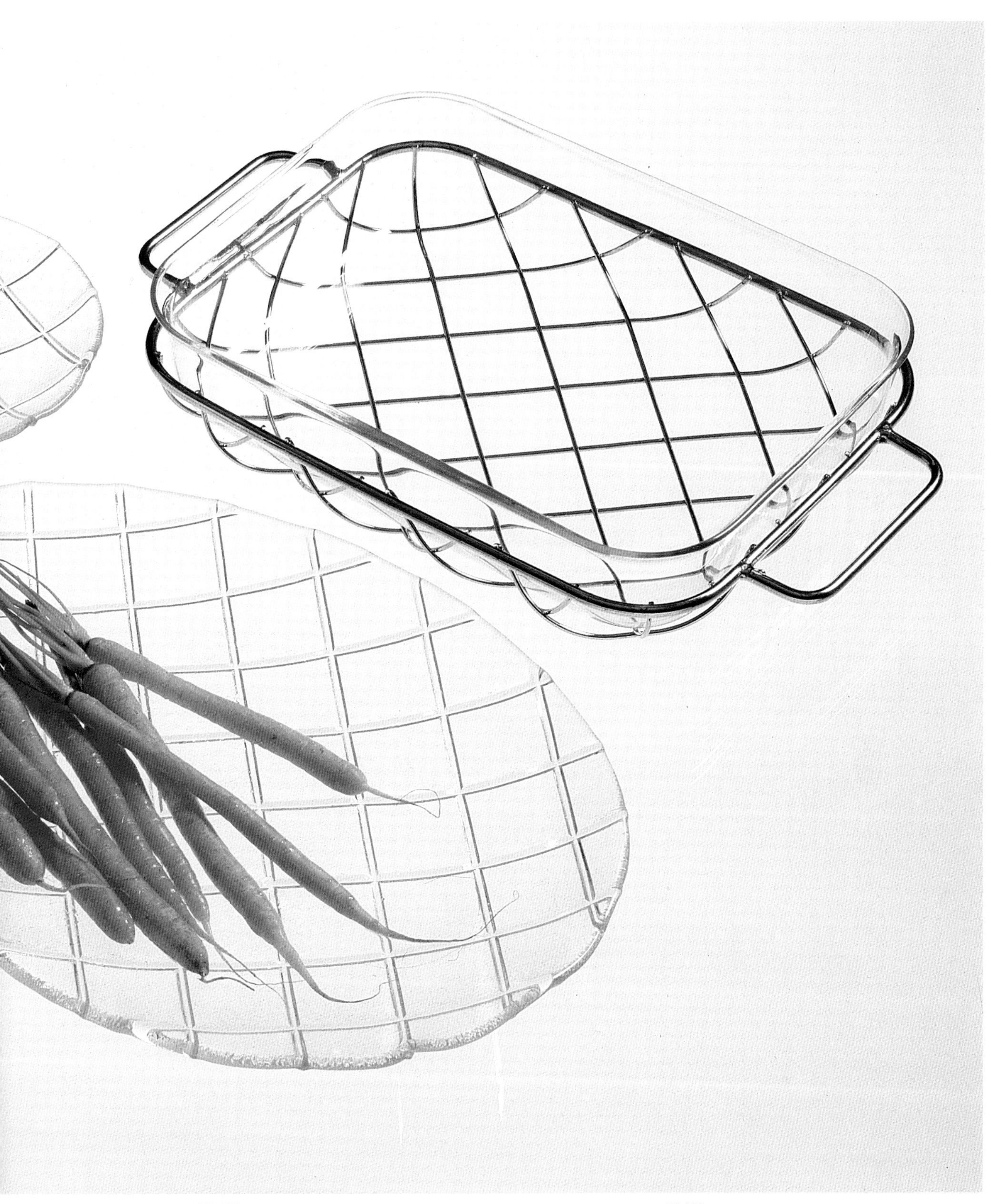

Not shown:
Visas ej:

78428
Dish,
1/box
Fat,
1/kart
Ø: 13¼″
Ø: 340 mm

78430
Cheese
platter,
1/box
Ostbricka,
1/kart
Ø: 15″
Ø: 380 mm

78435
Souffle dish,
1/box
Eldfast form,
1/kart
Ø: 6¼ × 6¼″
Ø: 160 ×
160 mm

78429
Serving plate, 1/box
Uppläggningsfat, 1/kart
Ø: 11 × 15″. 280 × 380 mm

78437
Casserole, 1/box
Eldfast form, 1/kart
Ø: 9 × 11½″. 230 × 295 mm

Maxim

Design: Anna Ehrner

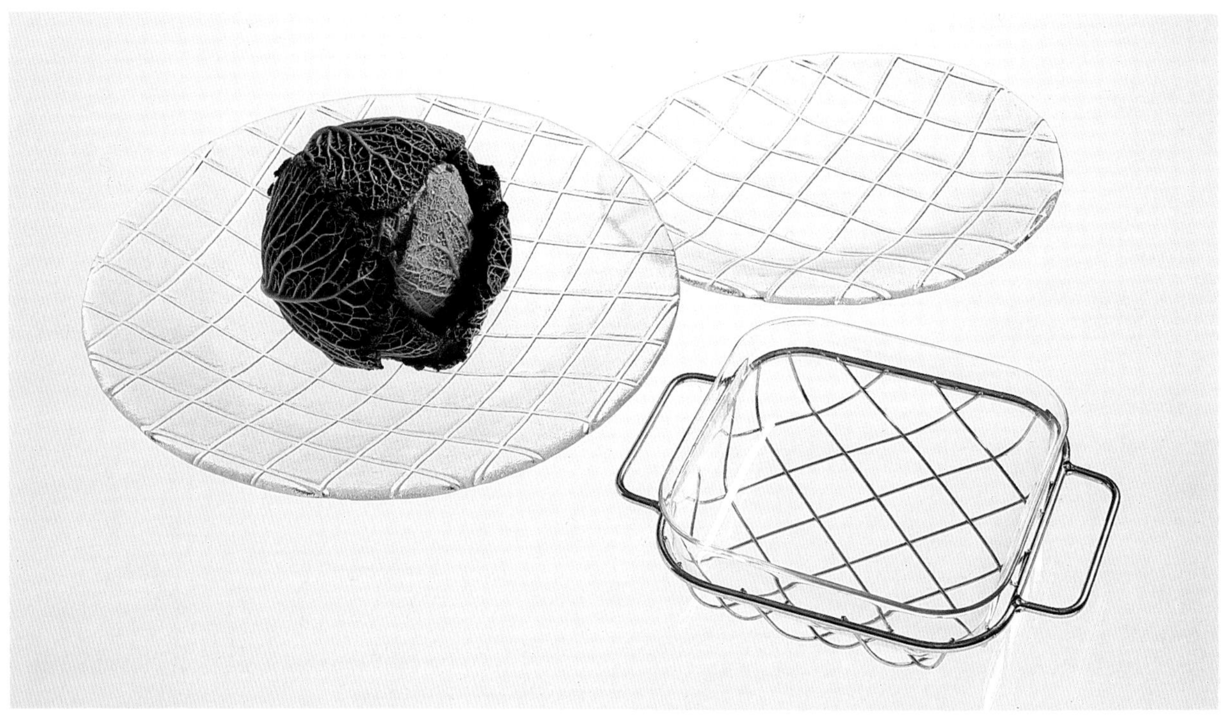

78431	78526	78436
Dish, 1/box	Fish plate, 2/box	Casserole, 1/box
Fat, 1/kart	Fisktallrik, 2/kart	Eldfast form, 1/kart
Ø: 15¾". 400 mm	Ø: 10×12½". 255×320 mm	Ø: 8×8". 208×208 mm

Maxim

Design: Anna Ehrner

58426	98425	58425	58427
Bowl, 1/box	Napkin holder, 1/box	Dessert bowl, 2/box	Bowl, 1/box
Skål, 1/kart	Servettställ, 1/kart	Dessertskål, 2/kart	Skål, 1/kart
Ø: 8". 200 mm		Ø: 6". 150 mm	Ø: 9". 230 mm

MATHILDA

DESIGN: ROLF SINNEMARK. HANDBLOWN. HANDBLÅST

NOT SHOWN:
VISAS EJ:

48292
VASE, 1/BOX
VAS, 1/KART
H: 6"
H: 150 MM

48293
VASE, 1/BOX
VAS, 1/KART
H: 7½". 190 MM

May

Design: Kjell Engman, Handblown. Handblåst

58638
Bowl
Skål
H: 6". 150 mm
Ø: 7¼". 105 mm

48637
Vase
Vas
H: 7¼". 185 mm

48638
Vase
Vas
H: 9¼". 235 mm

58637
Bowl
Skål
H: 4¼″. 110 mm
Ø: 5″. 130 mm

48636
Vase
Vas
H: 6″. 150 mm

58636
Bowl
Skål
H: 3″. 75 mm
Ø: 4″. 100 mm

Misty

Design: Bengt Edenfalk. Full Lead Crystal. Kristall

21907	21921	21903	21908	21905
Wine, 9 oz, 1/box	Champagne flute, 5¼ oz, 1/box	Wine, 2½ oz, 1/box	Wine, 10½ oz, 1/box	Wine, 5¼ oz, 1/box
Vin, 25 cl, 1/kart	Champagne hög, 15 cl, 1/kart	Vin, 7½ cl, 1/kart	Vin, 30 cl, 1/kart	Vin, 15 cl, 1/kart
H: 7¼". 185 mm	H: 8½". 215 mm	H: 5¾". 145 mm	H: [illegible]". 200 mm	H: 7". 175 mm
Ø: 3". 75 mm	Ø: [illegible]". 50 mm	Ø: 2". 50 mm	Ø: 3". 75 mm	Ø: 2¾". 70 mm

21962
CARAFE, 35 OZ, 1/BOX
KARAFF, 100 CL, 1/KART
H: 10¼". 265 MM

58512
BOWL, 1/BOX
SKÅL, 1/KART
H: 4½". 115 MM
Ø: 7". 180 MM

58513
BOWL, 1/BOX
SKÅL, 1/KART
H: 5¼". 135 MM
Ø: 8½". 215 MM

Monet

Design: Mats Jonasson. Full Lead Crystal. Kristall

57968
Bowl, 1/box. Skål, 1/kart
Ø: 5¾". 145 mm

Noblesse

Design: Sigurd Persson. Full Lead Crystal, Handblown, Cut. Kristall, Handblåst, Slipat

57872
Bowl
Skål
Ø: 6½". 165 mm

47872
Vase
Vas
H: 7". 180 mm
Ø: 4¾". 120 mm

57873
Bowl
Skål
Ø: 8". 200 mm

Nordic

Design: Kjell Engman. Handblown. Handblåst

58058
Bowl. Skål
H: 5¾". 145 mm Ø: 6¼". 160 mm

58056
Bowl. Skål
H: 2". 50 mm Ø: 2½". 65 mm

58057
Bowl. Skål
H: 3¾". 95 mm Ø: 4¼". 110 mm

November

Design: Kjell Engman. Handblown. Handblåst

58463
Bowl
Skål
Ø: 7". 175 mm

58462
Bowl
Skål
Ø: 5¼". 135 mm

48462
Vase
Vas
H: 8". 200 mm

October

Design: Kjell Engman. Handblown. Handblåst

58263
Bowl
Skål
H: 6″. 150 mm

58262
Bowl
Skål
H: 4″. 100 mm

48232
VASE
VAS
H: 9". 230 MM

48378
VASE
VAS
H: 6". 150 MM

58375
MINIATURE BOWL, 1/BOX
MINIATYRSKÅL, 1/KART
Ø: 2¾". 70 MM

Noble

Design: Göran Wärff. Full Lead Crystal, Handblown. Kristall, Handblåst

88508
Decanter, 26 oz
Karaff, 75 cl
H: 9". 225 mm

Optic

Design: Ulrica Hydman-Vallien. Handblown. Handblåst

Not shown:
Visas ej:
88108
Carafe,
35 oz
Karaff,
100 cl
H: 7″
H: 180 mm

88109
Carafe, 60 oz
Karaff, 175 cl
H: 8½″. 220 mm

Oktav

Design: Bertil Vallien. Handblown. Handblåst

98008	97923	97793	97828
Aquavit, 1½ oz, 2/box	Martini, 4¼ oz, 2/box	Wine, 12¼ oz, 2/box	Ice bucket, 1/box
Snaps, 4 cl, 2/kart	Martini, 12 cl, 2/kart	Vin, 35 cl, 2/kart	Ishink, 1/kart
H: 4¾". 120 mm	H: 6". 150 mm	H: 6½". 170 mm	H: 4½". 110 mm
Ø: 2". 50 mm	Ø: 4½". 110 mm	Ø: 3". 75 mm	Ø: 4¾". 120 mm

87793
CARAFE, 26 OZ, 1/BOX
KARAFF, 75 CL, 1/KART
H: 9". 230 MM

97922
WINE, 3½ OZ, 2/BOX
VIN, 9 CL, 2/KART
H: 5". 125 MM
Ø: 2". 50 MM

97825
WINE, 7 OZ, 2/BOX
VIN, 20 CL, 2/KART
H: 6¼". 160 MM
Ø: 2¾". 70 MM

97827
O F, 7 OZ, 2/BOX
O F, 20 CL, 2/KART
H: 3". 75 MM
Ø: 2¾". 70 MM

97924
CHAMPAGNE FLUTE, 4½ OZ, 2/BOX
CHAMPAGNE HÖG, 13 CL, 2/KART
H: 8½". 215 MM
Ø: 2". 50 MM

OKTAV

DESIGN: BERTIL VALLIEN. HANDBLOWN. HANDBLÅST

87794
53 OZ, 1/BOX • KANNA, 150 CL, 1/KART
H: 7½". 195 MM

57793
BOWL, 1/BOX. SKÅL, 1/KART
H: 4¾". 120 MM. Ø: 6½". 165 MM

57792
BOWL, 1/BOX. SKÅL, 1/KART
H: 3¼". 85 MM. Ø: 4½". 115 MM

57794
BOWL, 1/BOX. SKÅL, 1/K
H: 5¾". 145 MM. Ø: 7½". 1

OLIVIA

DESIGN: ANNA EHRNER. FULL LEAD CRYSTAL, HANDBLOWN. KRISTALL, HANDBLÅST

58028
BOWL, 1/BOX. SKÅL, 1/KART
H: 4½". 110 MM
Ø: 7". 175 MM

58027
BOWL, 1/BOX. SKÅL, 1/KART
H: 3". 75 MM
Ø: 5". 125 MM

48027
VASE. VAS
H: 8". 200 MM
Ø: 4½". 110 MM

OPUS

DESIGN: ROLF SINNEMARK. FULL LEAD CRYSTAL. KRISTALL

58270
BOWL, 1/BOX. SKÅL, 1/KART
H: 2¾". 70 MM. Ø: 4½". 110 MM

58372
BOWL, 1/BOX. SKÅL, 1/KART
H: 4". 100 MM. Ø: 6¼". 160 MM

58272
BOWL, 1/BOX. SKÅL, 1/KART
H: 2¾". 70 MM. Ø: 4½". 110 MM

OVAL

DESIGN: GÖRAN WÄRFF. FULL LEAD CRYSTAL. HANDBLOWN. KRISTALL, HANDBLÅST

77900
DISH, OVAL
FAT, OVALT
Ø: 9½ × 16½". 240 × 390 MM

Party

Design: Wärff

58316
Bowl, 1/box
Skål, 1/kart
H: 5½". 140 mm
Ø: 11". 275 mm

58510
Coupe, 2/box
Glasskål, 2/kart
H: 4". 100 mm
Ø: 4". 100 mm

Not shown:
Visas ej:

57285
Bowl, 1/box
Skål, 1/kart
Ø: 7¼″
Ø: 185 mm

58103
Bowl, footed, 1/box
Skål, på fot, 1/kart
H: 5¾″
H: 145 mm
Ø: 6″
Ø: 150 mm

68355
Hurricane, 1/box
Ljuslykta, 1/kart
H: 3″
H: 75 mm

58315
Bowl, 1/box
Skål, 1/kart
H: 7¼″. 185 mm
Ø: 7¼″. 185 mm

57348
Dessert bowl, 2/box
Dessertskål, 2/kart
Ø: 4½″. 115 mm

97283
Egg cup, 2/box
Äggkopp, 2/kart
H: 2½″. 65 mm

57284
Bowl, 1/box
Skål, 1/kart
Ø: 9″. 230 mm

PARTY

DESIGN: WÄRFF

78101
CAKE PLATE, 1/BOX
TÅRTFAT, 1/KART
Ø: 8½". 220 MM

97349
BEER, 2/BOX
ÖL, 2/KART
H: 5¼". 135 MM

NOT SHOWN:
VISAS EJ:

78102
CAKE PLATE, 1/BOX
TÅRTFAT, 1/KART
Ø: 12½"
Ø: 320 MM

98510
CHEESE COVER, 1/BOX
OSTKUPA, 1/KART
H: 7½". 195 MM
Ø: 11". 275 MM

57283
AVOCADO BOWL, 2/BOX
AVOCADOSKÅL, 2/KART
Ø: 3½ × 6¼". 90 × 160 MM

57288
BOWL, 1/BOX
SKÅL, 1/KART
Ø: 4¾". 120 MM

PARTY

DESIGN: WÄRFF

77305
PLATE, CRAB, 2/BOX
FAT, KRABBA, 2/KART
Ø: 10¼". 260 MM

57804
BOWL, 1/BOX
SKÅL, 1/KART
H: 2½". 65 MM
Ø: 8¼". 210 MM

77154
PLATE, FISH, 1/BOX
FAT, FISK, 1/KART
Ø: 13". 330 MM

NOT SHOWN:
VISAS EJ:

57706
FRUIT BOWL,
1/BOX
FRUKTSKÅL,
1/KART
H: 2¾″
H: 70 MM
Ø: 7¼″
Ø: 185 MM

57805
FRUIT BOWL,
1/BOX
FRUKTSKÅL,
1/KART
H: 2½″
H: 65 MM
Ø: 12¼″
Ø: 310 MM

77153
PLATE, FISH,
2/BOX
FAT, FISK,
2/KART
Ø: 10¼″
Ø: 260 MM

97289
BUTTER DISH, 1/BOX
SMÖRBYTTA, 1/KART
Ø: 7½ × 6″. 190 × 155 MM

57287
GRAPEFRUIT BOWL, 2/BOX
GRAPEFRUKTSKÅL, 2/KART
Ø: 6½″. 165 MM

57707
FRUIT BOWL, 1/BOX
FRUKTSKÅL, 1/KART
H: 3″. 75 MM
Ø: 10½″. 270 MM

PARTY

DESIGN: WÄRFF

78315
DISH, 1/BOX
FAT, 1/KART
Ø: 15¾ × 11¾". 400 × 300 MM

97505
CHEESE PLATE
OSTBRICKA
Ø: 10½". 270 MM

77286
PLATE, 1/BOX
FAT, 1/KART
Ø: 13", 330 MM

Not shown:
Visas ej:

57346
Bowl, 2/box
Skål, 2/kart
Ø: 6½″
Ø: 170 mm

77285
Plate,
2/box
Tallrik,
2/kart
Ø: 10″
Ø: 255 mm

78510
Dish, 1/box
Fat, 1/kart
Ø: 15¼″
Ø: 390 mm

97506
Cheese plate,
1/box
Ostbricka,
1/kart
Ø: 13¾″
Ø: 350 mm

78103
Cake plate, 1/box
kakfat, 1/kart
Ø: 17 × 7½″. 430 × 190 mm

57345
Dessert bowl, 2/box
Dessertskål, 2/kart
Ø: 5½″. 140 mm

77283
Small plate, 2/box
Assiett, 2/kart
Ø: 7″. 180 mm

Party Marina

Design: Göran Wärff

78511
Plate, Fish, 2/box
Tallrik, Fisk, 2/kart
Ø: 10×12½". 255×320 mm

78514
Plate, Fish, 2/box
Tallrik, Spätta, 2/kart
Ø: 10×12½". 255×320 mm

NOT SHOWN:
VISAS EJ:

78512
PLATE,
LOBSTER,
2/BOX
TALLRIK,
HUMMER,
2/KART
Ø: 10 × 12½".
Ø: 255 ×
320 MM

78513
PLATE,
CRAB,
2/BOX
TALLRIK,
KRABBA,
2/KART
Ø: 10 × 12½".
Ø: 255 ×
320 MM

78515
SERVING PLATE, 1/BOX
UPPLÄGGNINGSFAT, 1/KART
Ø: 15¼". 390 MM

PALACE

DESIGN: BENGT EDENFALK. FULL LEAD CRYSTAL, HANDBLOWN. KRISTALL, HANDBLÅST

48022
VASE, HEXAGONAL
VAS, 6-KT
H: 8¼". 210 MM

48023
VASE, HEXAGONAL
VAS, 6-KT
H: 9¼". 235 MM

48021
VASE, HEXAGONAL
VAS, 6-KT
H: 6½". 165 MM

Picnic

Design: Kjell Engman. Full Lead Crystal. Kristall

58620
Bowl, 1/box. Skål, 1/kart
H: 4″. 100 mm. Ø: 7¼″. 185 mm

58619
Bowl, 1/box. Skål, 1/kart
H: 3″. 75 mm. Ø: 5¼″. 135 mm

58621
Bowl, 1/box. Skål, 1/kart
H: 5″. 125 mm. Ø: 9″. 225 mm

Picnic

Design: Kjell Engman. Full Lead Crystal. Kristall

78406
Dish, 1/box
Fat, 1/kart
Ø: 13″. 330 mm

78504
Small plate, 2/box
Assiett, 2/kart
Ø: 7½″. 190 mm

78405
Dish, 1/box
Fat, 1/kart
Ø: 12½″. 320 mm

PIPPI

DESIGN: KOSTA BODA TRADITIONAL. HANDBLOWN. HANDBLÅST

29846	29842	29862	29825	29844
TUMBLER, 12¼ OZ	TUMBLER, 3½ OZ	DECANTER, 21 OZ	AQUAVIT, 2 OZ	TUMBLER, 9 OZ
TUMBLER, 35 CL	TUMBLER, 10 CL	KARAFF, 60 CL	SNAPS, 5 CL	TUMBLER, 25 CL
H: 6¼". 160 MM	H: 4¼". 110 MM	H: 12½". 320 MM	H: 4¾". 120 MM	H: 7". 175 MM
Ø: 2¾". 70 MM	Ø: 2". 50 MM	Ø: 3". 75 MM	Ø: 1½". 40 MM	Ø: 2". 50 MM

29826	29881	29801	86397	29821
Cocktail, 3½ oz	Ice bucket, 26½ oz, 1/box	Aquavit, 1 oz	Jug, 26½ oz	Champagne, 4 oz
Cocktail, 10 cl	Ishink, 75 cl, 1/kart	Snaps, 3 cl	Kanna, 75 cl	Champagne, 12 cl
H: 2¾". 70 mm	H: 5". 130 mm	H: 3¼". 85 mm	H: 10¼". 260 mm	H: 6". 150 mm
Ø: 2¼". 60 mm	Ø: 5". 130 mm	Ø: 1¼". 35 mm	Ø: 3¼". 85 mm	Ø: 1¾". 45 mm

PIPPI

DESIGN: KOSTA BODA TRADITIONAL. HANDBLOWN. HANDBLÅST

29849	86399	29847	29831
O F, 5¼ OZ	DECANTER, 26¼ OZ	TUMBLER, 10¼ OZ	CHAMPAGNE, 6 OZ
O F, 15 CL	KARAFF, 75 CL	TUMBLER, 30 CL	CHAMPAGNE, 17 CL
H: 3". 75 MM	H: 9¼". 235 MM	H: 3¾". 95 MM	H: 7½". 190 MM
Ø: 2¾". 70 MM	Ø: 4¾". 120 MM	Ø: 3½". 90 MM	Ø: 1¾". 45 MM

29879
ICE BUCKET, 17 OZ, 1/BOX
ISHINK, 50 CL, 1/KART
H: 4½". 110 MM
Ø: 4". 100 MM

46245
VASE, 1/BOX
VAS, 1/KART
H: 7½". 195 MM

29850
D O F, 7 OZ
D O F, 20 CL
H: 3½". 90 MM
Ø: 3". 75 MM

29805
TUMBLER, 5¼ OZ
TUMBLER, 15 CL
H: 5". 130 MM
Ø: 2". 50 MM

PLAZA

DESIGN: SIGURD PERSSON. FULL LEAD CRYSTAL, HANDBLOWN. KRISTALL, HANDBLÅST

47931
VASE
VAS
H: 5″. 130 MM

57846
BOWL
SKÅL
H: 2¾″. 70 MM
Ø: 5½″. 140 MM

47848
VASE
VAS
H: 8¼″. 210 MM

Not shown:
Visas ej:

47846
Vase
Vas
H: 4¾″
H: 120 mm

57848
Bowl
Skål
H: 4″. 100 mm
Ø: 8¼″. 210 mm

47847
Vase
Vas
H: 7″. 175 mm

57847
Bowl
Skål
H: 3″. 75 mm
Ø: 6¼″. 160 mm

Poem

Design: Ulrica Hydman-Vallien. Handblown, Handpainted. Handblåst, Handmålad

58220
Bowl, 1/box
Skål, 1/kart
H: 3½". 90 mm
Ø: 5". 130 mm

48284
Vase, 1/box
Vas, 1/kart
H: 7". 180 mm

48282
Vase, 1/box
Vas, 1/kart
H: 3½". 90 mm

58222
Bowl, 1/box
Skål, 1/kart
H: 4¾". 120 mm
Ø: 7½". 190 mm

58221
Bowl, 1/box
Skål, 1/kart
H. 6". 150 mm
Ø: 5". 130 mm

48283
Vase, 1/box
Vas, 1/kart
H: 4¾". 120 mm

Polar

Design: Göran Wärff. Full Lead Crystal. Kristall

67714
Hurricane, 1/box. Ljuslykta, 1/kart
H: 3". 75 mm

Perfume Bottles

Design: Vicke Lindstrand. Full Lead Crystal, Handblown. Kristall, Handblåst

98310
Perfume bottle
Flakong
H: 3½". 90 mm

91856
Perfume bottle, Pear, 1/box
Flakong, Päron, 1/kart
H: 3". 75 mm

98311
Perfume bottle
Flakong
H: 4". 100 mm

91855
Perfume bottle, Apple, 1/box
Flakong, Äpple, 1/kart
H: 2". 55 mm

PRESIDENT

DESIGN: GÖRAN WÄRFF. FULL LEAD CRYSTAL, HANDBLOWN, CUT. KRISTALL, HANDBLÅST, SLIPAD.

NOT SHOWN:
VISAS EJ:

98415
DECANTER AND
6 GLASSES,
IN WOODEN
CASE.
KARAFF OCH
6 GLAS,
I TRÄSCHATULL

88416
DECANTER, 28 OZ
KARAFF, 80 CL
H: 9¼". 235 MM

98416
GLASS, 9 OZ
GLAS, 25 CL
H: 3". 75 MM
Ø; 3½". 90 MM

PRINCE

DESIGN: WÄRFF. FULL LEAD CRYSTAL, HANDBLOWN, CUT. KRISTALL, HANDBLÅST, SLIPAD.

29005	29003	86207	29007	29025
WINE, 5¼ OZ	WINE, 2¼ OZ	DECANTER, 23 OZ	WINE, 9 OZ	AQUAVIT, 1 OZ
VIN, 15 CL	VIN, 7½ CL	KARAFF, 65 CL	VIN, 25 CL	SNAPS, 3 CL
H: 6". 150 MM	H: 4¾". 120 MM	H: 9". 230 MM	H: 6½". 170 MM	H: 5¼". 135 MM
Ø: 3". 75 MM	Ø: 2¾". 60 MM	Ø: 5". 125 MM	Ø: 3¼". 85 MM	Ø: 2". 50 MM

29024
LIQUEUR BOWL, 1 OZ
LIKÖRSKÅL, 3 CL
H: 3¾". 95 MM
Ø: 2¼". 60 MM

29021
CHAMPAGNE FLUTE, 5½ OZ
CHAMPAGNE HÖG, 16 CL
H: 8½". 220 MM
Ø: 3¼". 85 MM

29079
ICE BUCKET, 17 OZ
ISHINK, 50 CL
H: 4¼". 110 MM
Ø: 4½". 115 MM

29004
WINE, 3½ OZ
VIN, 10 CL
H: 5½". 140 MM
Ø: 2½". 65 MM

29001
WINE, 1 OZ
VIN, 2½ CL
H: 4". 105 MM
Ø: 1¾". 45 MM

PRINCE

DESIGN: WÄRFF. FULL LEAD CRYSTAL, HANDBLOWN, CUT. KRISTALL, HANDBLÅST, SLIPAD.

29049	29052	29046	29051	66201	66200	66202	29050
O F, 7 OZ	TUMBLER, 3 OZ	TUMBLER, 12¼ OZ	COCKTAIL, 5¼ OZ	CANDLESTICK	CANDLESTICK	CANDLESTICK	D O F, 10½ OZ
O F, 20 CL	TUMBLER, 10 CL	TUMBLER, 35 CL	COCKTAIL, 15 CL	LJUSSTAKE	LJUSSTAKE	LJUSSTAKE	D O F, 30 CL
H: 3¼". 85 MM	H: 2½". 65 MM	H: 6". 150 MM	H: 2¾". 70 MM	H: 9". 220 MM	H: 7". 170 MM	H: 10½". 270 MM	H: 4". 100 MM
Ø: 3¼". 85 MM	Ø: 2¼". 60 MM	Ø: 3". 75 MM	Ø: 2¾". 70 MM				Ø: 3¾". 95 MM

86200	56190	29062	76154	56191
DECANTER, 17 OZ	BOWL	DECANTER, 23 OZ	ASHTRAY, 1/BOX	BOWL
KARAFF, 50 CL	SKÅL	KARAFF, 65 CL	ASKFAT, 1/KART	SKÅL
H: 9¼". 235 MM	Ø: 4¾". 120 MM	H: 8½". 220 MM	Ø: 5". 130 MM	Ø: 6½". 165 MM
		Ø: 2¾". 70 MM		

Puzzle

Design: Bertil Vallien. Full Lead Crystal. Kristall.

78544
Ashtray, 1/box. Askfat, 1/kart
4¼ × 4¼ × 3¾". 108 × 108 × 95 mm

78543
Ashtray, 1/box. Askfat, 1/kart
3 × 3 × 3". 75 × 75 × 75 mm

Prism

Design: Vicke Lindstrand. Full Lead Crystal, Cut, Engraved. Kristall, Slipad, Graverad

92415
Bird Cage, 1/box
Fågelbur, 1/kart
H: 4". 100 mm

92412
Deer Park
Träd och Hjortar
H: 6½". 170 mm

97105
School of Fish
Fiskstim
H: 4". 100 mm

97257
Ballet
Balett
H: 4". 100 mm

RAINDROP

DESIGN: GÖRAN WÄRFF. FULL LEAD CRYSTAL, HANDBLOWN. KRISTALL, HANDBLÅST

47800	47801	47802
BUD VASE, 1/BOX	BUD VASE, 1/BOX	VASE, 1/BOX
ORKIDÉVAS, 1/KART	ORKIDÉVAS, 1/KART	VAS, 1/KART
H: 8½". 215 MM	H: 11". 275 MM	H: 5½". 140 MM

RAINBOW

DESIGN: BERTIL VALLIEN. HANDBLOWN. HANDBLÅST

48381	48290	48382	48227	48224
MINIATURE VASE, GREEN, 1/BOX	VASE, 1/BOX	MINIATURE VASE, BLUE, 1/BOX	VASE, 1/BOX	VASE, 1/BOX
MINIATYRVAS, GRÖN, 1/KART	VAS, 1/KART	MINIATYRVAS, BLÅ, 1/KART	VAS, 1/KART	VAS, 1/KART
H: 5¼″. 135 MM	H: 10″. 255 MM	H: 3″. 75 MM	H: 8″. 200 MM	H: 5½″. 140 MM

48288
VASE, OVAL, 1/BOX
VAS, OVAL, 1/KART
H: 7½". 195 MM

48380
MINIATURE VASE, WHITE, 1/BOX
MINIATYRVAS, VIT, 1/KART
H: 2¾". 70 MM

48287
VASE, 1/BOX
VAS, 1/KART
H: 9". 230 MM

RAINBOW

DESIGN: BERTIL VALLIEN. HANDBLOWN. HANDBLÅST

58286
BOWL, 1/BOX
SKÅL, 1/KART
H: 6¼". 160 MM
Ø: 8¼". 210 MM

58285
BOWL, 1/BOX
SKÅL, 1/KART
H: 4¼". 110 MM
Ø: 5¼". 135 MM

48289
VASE, 1/BOX
VAS, 1/KART
H: 9½". 240 MM

48383
MINIATURE VASE, WHITE, 1/BOX
MINIATYRVAS, VIT, 1/KART
H: 3½". 90 MM

68312
OIL LAMP, 1/BOX
OLJELAMPA, 1/KART
H: 2¾". 70 MM

58380
MINIATURE BOWL, PINK, 1/BOX
MINIATYRSKÅL, ROSA, 1/KART
Ø: 2½". 60 MM

48225
VASE, 1/BOX
VAS, 1/KART
H: 3¼". 85 MM

48226
VASE, 1/BOX
VAS, 1/KART
H: 6½". 170 MM

48223
VASE, 1/BOX
VAS, 1/KART
H: 3". 75 MM

Rainbow

Design: Bertil Vallien. Handblown. Handblåst

98332
Ice bucket
Ishink
H: 5¾". 145 mm
Ø: 5½". 135 mm

98330
D O F, 10¼ oz
D O F, 30 cl
H: 4". 100 mm
Ø: 3". 75 mm

98329
COCKTAIL, 7 OZ
COCKTAIL, 20 CL
H: 3¼". 85 MM
Ø: 3". 75 MM

98331
HIGHBALL, 12¼ OZ
GROGGLAS, 35 CL
H: 6". 150 MM
Ø: 2½". 65 MM

88325
DECANTER
KARAFF
H: 10½". 270 MM

REGAL

DESIGN: BENGT EDENFALK. FULL LEAD CRYSTAL. KRISTALL

68514	68512	68513
CANDLESTICK, 1/BOX	CANDLESTICK, 1/BOX	CANDLESTICK, 1/BOX
LJUSSTAKE, 1/KART	LJUSSTAKE, 1/KART	LJUSSTAKE, 1/KART
H: 10″. 255 MM	H: 5½″. 140 MM	H: 7½″. 195 MM

Rhombus

Design: Kjell Engman. Full Lead Crystal. Kristall

68502	68501	68503
Candlestick, 1/box	Candlestick, 1/box	Candlestick, 1/box
Ljusstake, 1/kart	Ljusstake, 1/kart	Ljusstake, 1/kart
H: 5¼". 135 mm	H: 3". 75 mm	H: 7½". 190 mm

Rhapsody

Design: Kjell Engman

57839
Bowl, footed, 1/box
Skål, på fot, 1/kart
H: 5". 125 mm
Ø: 4½". 110 mm

57837
Bowl, 1/box
Skål, 1/kart
H: 4". 100 mm
Ø: 6". 150 mm

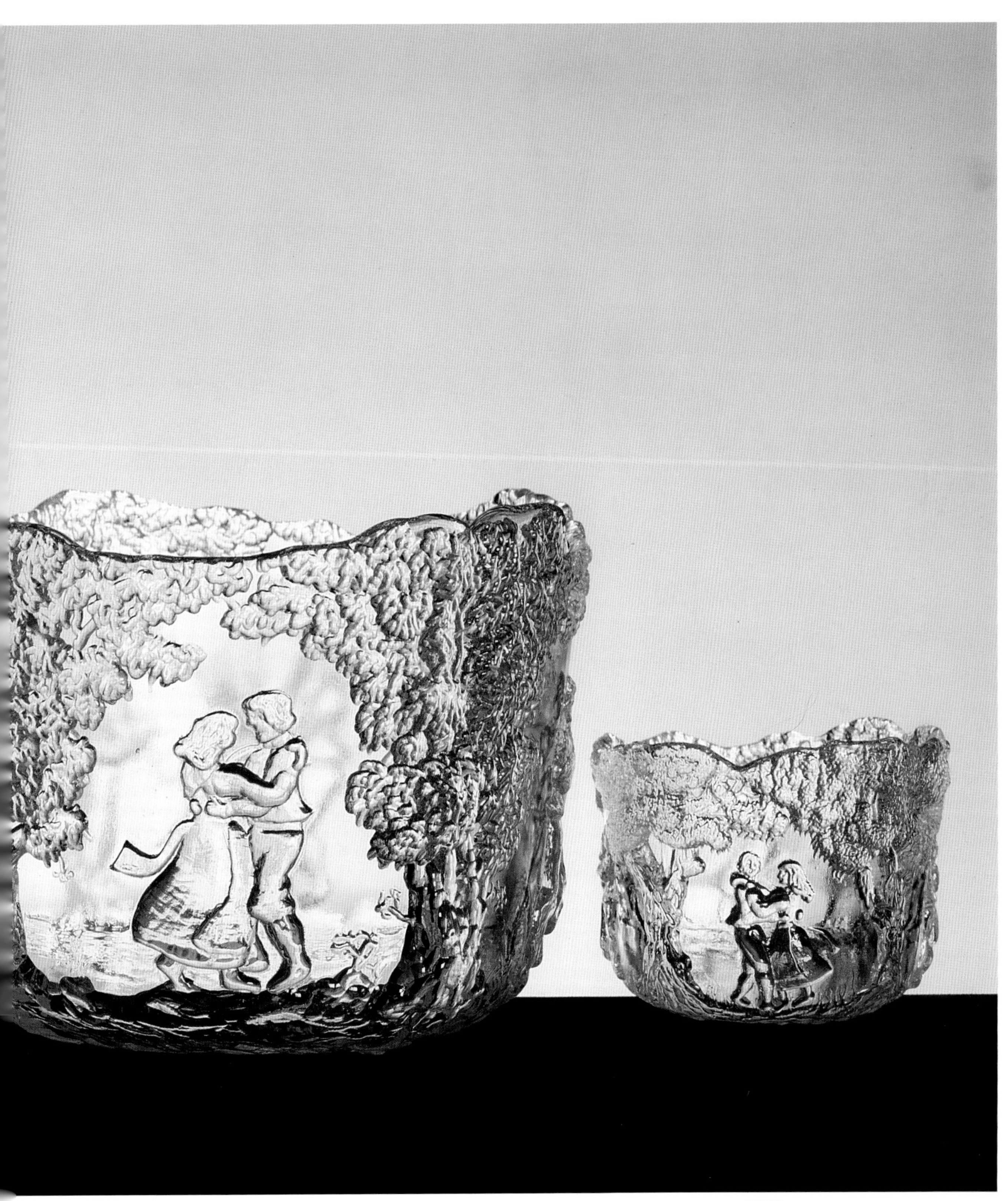

57838
BOWL, 1/BOX
SKÅL, 1/KART
H: 5½". 140 MM
Ø: 7½". 190 MM

57920
BOWL, 1/BOX
SKÅL, 1/KART
H: 3". 75 MM
Ø: 4". 100 MM

Rideau

Design: Gun Lindblad. Full Lead Crystal, Handblown, Cut. Kristall, Handblåst, Slipad

48501
Vase
Vas
H: 6½". 170 mm
Ø: 5". 130 mm

48503
Vase
Vas
H: 12¼". 315 mm
Ø: 5". 125 mm

58501
Bowl
Skål
H: 4¼". 110 mm
Ø: 6½". 170 mm

NOT SHOWN:
VISAS EJ:

58502
BOWL
SKÅL
H: 5″
H: 130 MM
Ø: 8¼″
Ø: 210 MM

48502
VASE
VAS
H: 8½″. 215 MM
Ø: 6½″. 170 MM

58503
BOWL
SKÅL
H: 6″. 155 MM
Ø: 10″. 250 MM

Roman

Design: Bengt Edenfalk. Full Lead Crystal. Kristall

58635
Bowl, 1/box
Skål, 1/kart
H: 4¼". 110 mm
Ø: 6½". 165 mm

58633
Bowl, 1/box
Skål, 1/kart
H: 3". 75 mm
Ø: 4½". 115 mm

58634
Bowl, 1/box
Skål, 1/kart
H: 4". 100 mm
Ø: 5¾". 145 mm

Rondo

Design: Wärff. Handblown. Handblåst

26005	26006	26003	26081
Wine, 5¼ oz	Wine, 7 oz	Wine, 2½ oz	Ice bucket, 1/box
Vin, 15 cl	Vin, 20 cl	Vin, 7½ cl	Ishink, 1/kart
H: 4¼". 110 mm	H: 5". 130 mm	H: 4". 100 mm	H: 4¾". 120 mm
Ø: 2¼". 60 mm	Ø: 2¾". 70 mm	Ø: 2". 50 mm	Ø: 5". 130 mm

26062	26063	26001	26008	26049
Decanter, 28 oz	Decanter, 53 oz	Aquavit, 1 oz	Wine, 10½ oz	O F, 7 oz
Karaff, 80 cl	Karaff, 150 cl	Snaps, 2½ cl	Vin, 30 cl	O F, 20 cl
H: 9½". 240 mm	H: 11¾". 300 mm	H: 3¾". 95 mm	H: 6". 150 mm	H: 4". 100 mm
		Ø: 1½". 40 mm	Ø: 3½". 90 mm	Ø: 3". 75 mm

H:

Royal

Design: Anna Ehrner. Handblown, Full Lead Crystal. Handblåst, Kristall

47756
Vase
Vas
H: 7″. 180 mm

57756
Bowl
Skål
Ø: 8″. 200 mm

47833
VASE
VAS
H: 8¼″. 210 MM

47755
VASE
VAS
H: 6″. 150 MM

Rose

Design: Rolf Sinnemark. Full Lead Crystal. Kristall

68201
Hurricane, 1/box. Ljuslykta, 1/kart
H: 3". 75 mm

Sails

Design: Göran Wärff. Full Lead Crystal, Cut. Kristall, Slipad

98003	98001	98002	97939
Sculpture, wooden stand	Sculpture, wooden stand	Sculpture, wooden stand	Drop, dark wooden stand
Skulptur, träsockel	Skulptur, träsockel	Skulptur, träsockel	Droppe, mörk träsockel
H: 5". 130 mm	H: 3½". 90 mm	H: 7". 175 mm	H: 8¼". 210 mm
Ø: 3¾ × 3¾". 95 × 95 mm	Ø: 3 × 3". 75 × 75 mm	Ø: 3 × 3". 75 × 75 mm	

Serenade

Design: Bengt Edenfalk. Full Lead Crystal, Handblown. Kristall, Handblåst

Not shown:
Visas ej:

48447
Vase
Vas
H: 6".
H: 150 mm

48448
Vase
Vas
H: 7½". 190 mm

Spiral

Design: Rolf Sinnemark. Handblown. Handblåst

60024
Candlestick
Ljusstake
H: 10″. 250 mm

60023
Candlestick
Ljusstake
H: 7″. 180 mm

60025
Candlestick
Ljusstake
H: 12½″. 320 mm

Seafood

Design: Paul Hoff

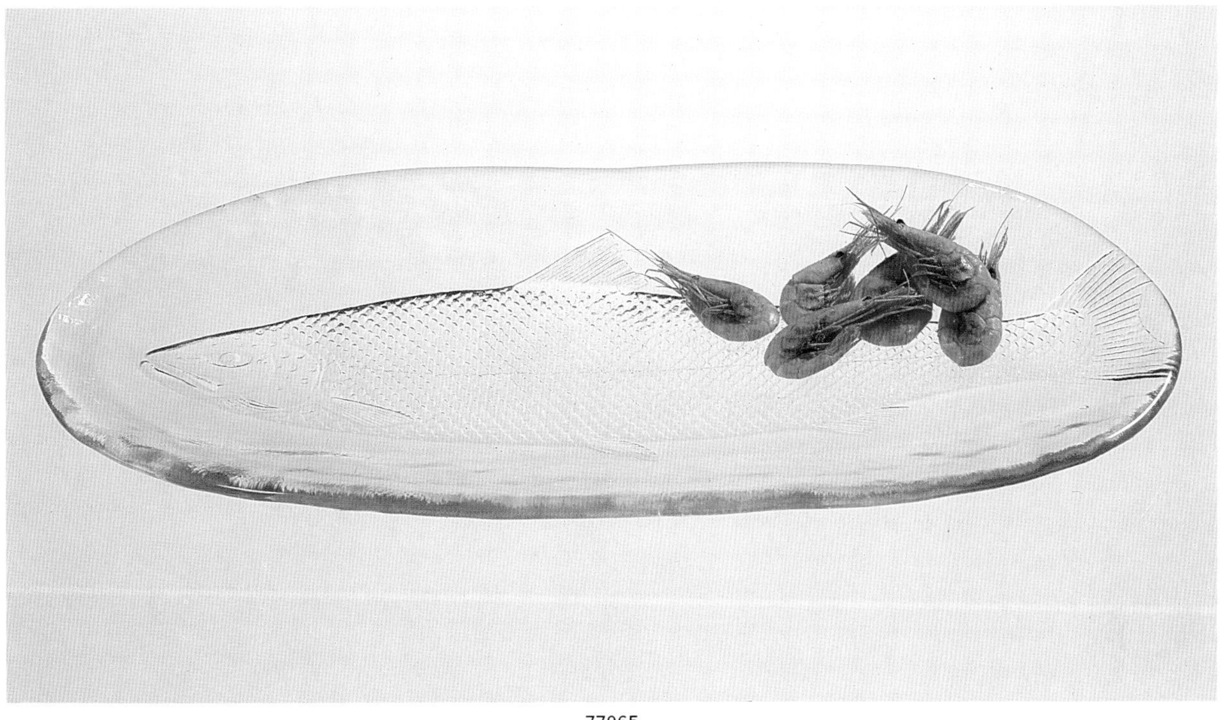

77965
Dish, Salmon, 1/box. Fat, Lax, 1/kart
L: 19¾". 500 mm

Sapphire

Design: Bengt Edenfalk. Full Lead Crystal. Kristall

68517	68515	68516
Candlestick, 1/box	Candlestick, 1/box	Candlestick, 1/box
Ljusstake, 1/kart	Ljusstake, 1/kart	Ljusstake, 1/kart
H: 10". 255 mm	H: 7". 180 mm	H: 8¼". 210 mm

Sweden

Design: Kjell Engman

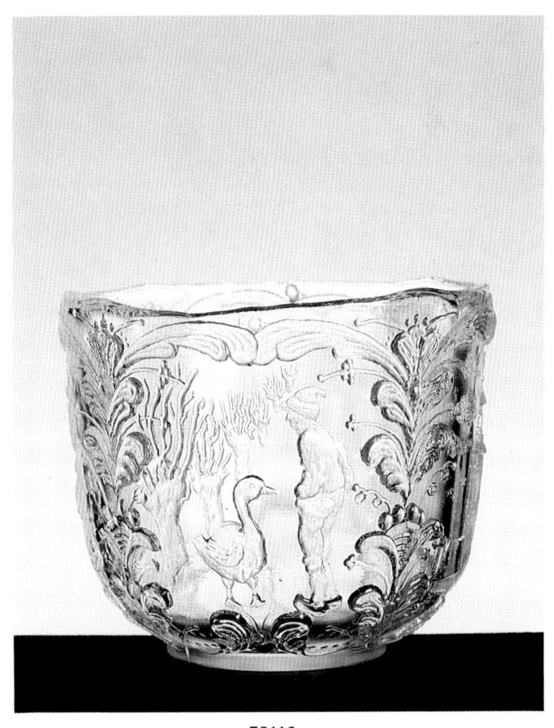

58112
Bowl, 1/box. Skål, 1/kart
H: 4½". 115 mm
Ø: 5½". 140 mm

Sir

Design: Göran Wärff. Full Lead Crystal, Handblown, Cut. Kristall, Handblåst, Slipad

22481
Ice bucket
Ishink
H: 6½". 170 mm
Ø; 6". 155 mm

88401
Decanter, 28 oz
Karaff, 80 cl
H: 10". 250 mm

NOT SHOWN:
VISAS EJ:

98420
DECANTER
AND 6 OF,
IN CASE.
KARAFF
OCH 6 OF,
I SCHATULL.

22449	22446	22451
O F, 5¾ OZ	HIGHBALL, 12½ OZ	COCKTAIL, 3¼ OZ
O F, 15 CL	GROGGLAS, 35 CL	COCKTAIL, 10 CL
H: 3". 75 MM	H: 6½". 165 MM	H: 2¾". 70 MM
Ø: 3". 75 MM	Ø: 2¾". 70 MM	Ø: 2½". 65 MM

SNOWBALL

DESIGN: ANN WÄRFF. FULL LEAD CRYSTAL. KRISTALL

NOT SHOWN:
VISAS EJ:

67352
HURRICANE, RED, 6/BOX
LJUSLYKTA, RÖD, 6/KART
H: 2¾"
H: 70 MM

67350
HURRICANE, 6/BOX. LJUSLYKTA, 6/KART
H: 2¾". 70 MM

67353
HURRICANE, 1/BOX. LJUSLYKTA, 1/KART
H: 3½". 90 MM

67800
HURRICANE, 1/BOX. LJUSLYKTA, 1/KART
H: 2¼". 60 MM

SUNFLOWER

DESIGN: WÄRFF. FULL LEAD CRYSTAL. KRISTALL

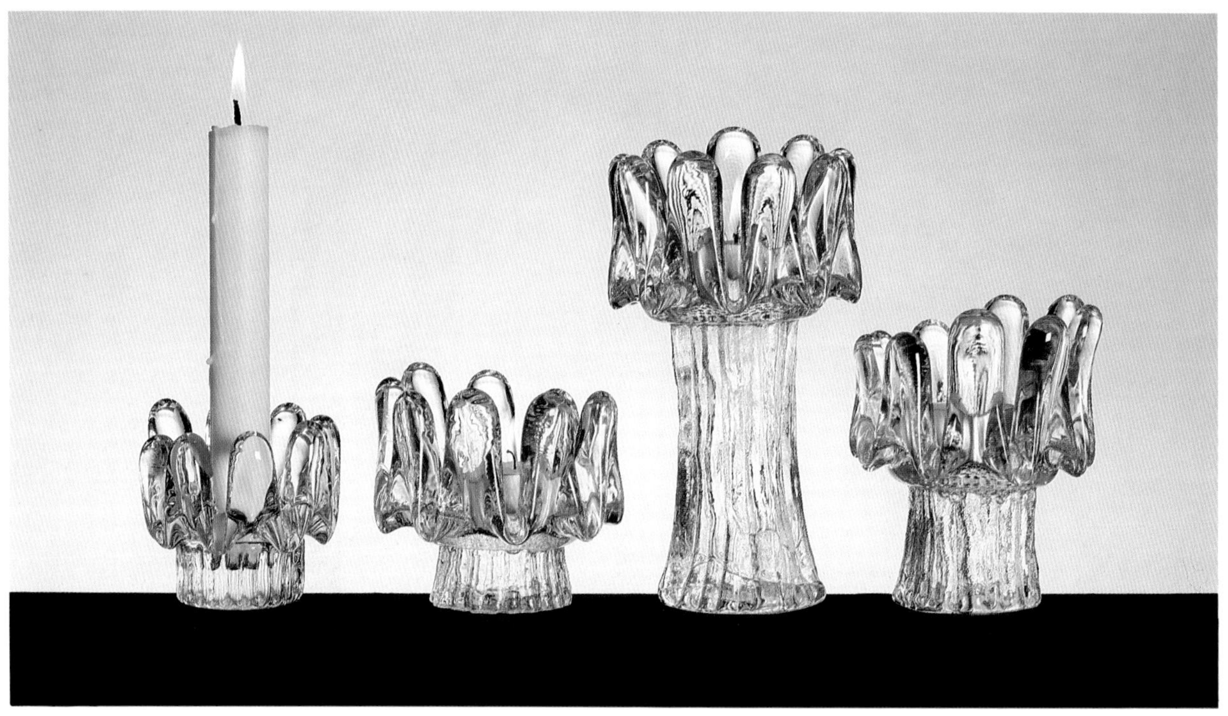

97124
CANDLESTICK, 1/BOX
LJUSSTAKE, 1/KART
H: 2½". 65 MM
Ø: 3". 75 MM

97127
CANDLESTICK WITH CANDLE, 1/BOX
LJUSSTAKE MED LJUS, 1/KART
H: 3½". 90 MM
Ø: 4". 100 MM

97129
CANDLESTICK WITH CANDLE, 1/BOX
LJUSSTAKE MED LJUS, 1/KART
H: 7". 180 MM
Ø: 4". 100 MM

97128
CANDLESTICK WITH CANDLE, 1/BOX
LJUSSTAKE MED LJUS, 1/KART
H: 5". 130 MM
Ø: 4". 100 MM

SOLITAIRE

DESIGN: KJELL ENGMAN. FULL LEAD CRYSTAL. KRISTALL

68406
HURRICANE, 1/BOX
LJUSLYKTA, 1/KART
H: 3¼". 85 MM

SPIN

DESIGN: BERTIL VALLIEN. HANDBLOWN. HANDBLÅST

VASE, 1/BOX
VAS, 1/KART
H: 9". 230 MM
48415 BLACK LINE. SVART SLINGA

BOWL, 1/BOX
SKÅL, 1/KART
Ø: 7½". 190 MM
58413 BLACK LINE. SVART SLINGA

Vase, 1/box
Vas, 1/kart
H: 7½". 195 mm
48414 Black line. Svart slinga
48411 Clear line. Klar slinga

Vase, 1/box
Vas, 1/kart
H: 7". 180 mm
48413 Black line. Svart slinga
48410 Clear line. Klar slinga

Bowl, 1/box
Skål, 1/kart
Ø: 5¾". 145 mm
58412 Black line. Svart slinga
58410 Clear line. Klar slinga

Tempera

Design: Anna Ehrner

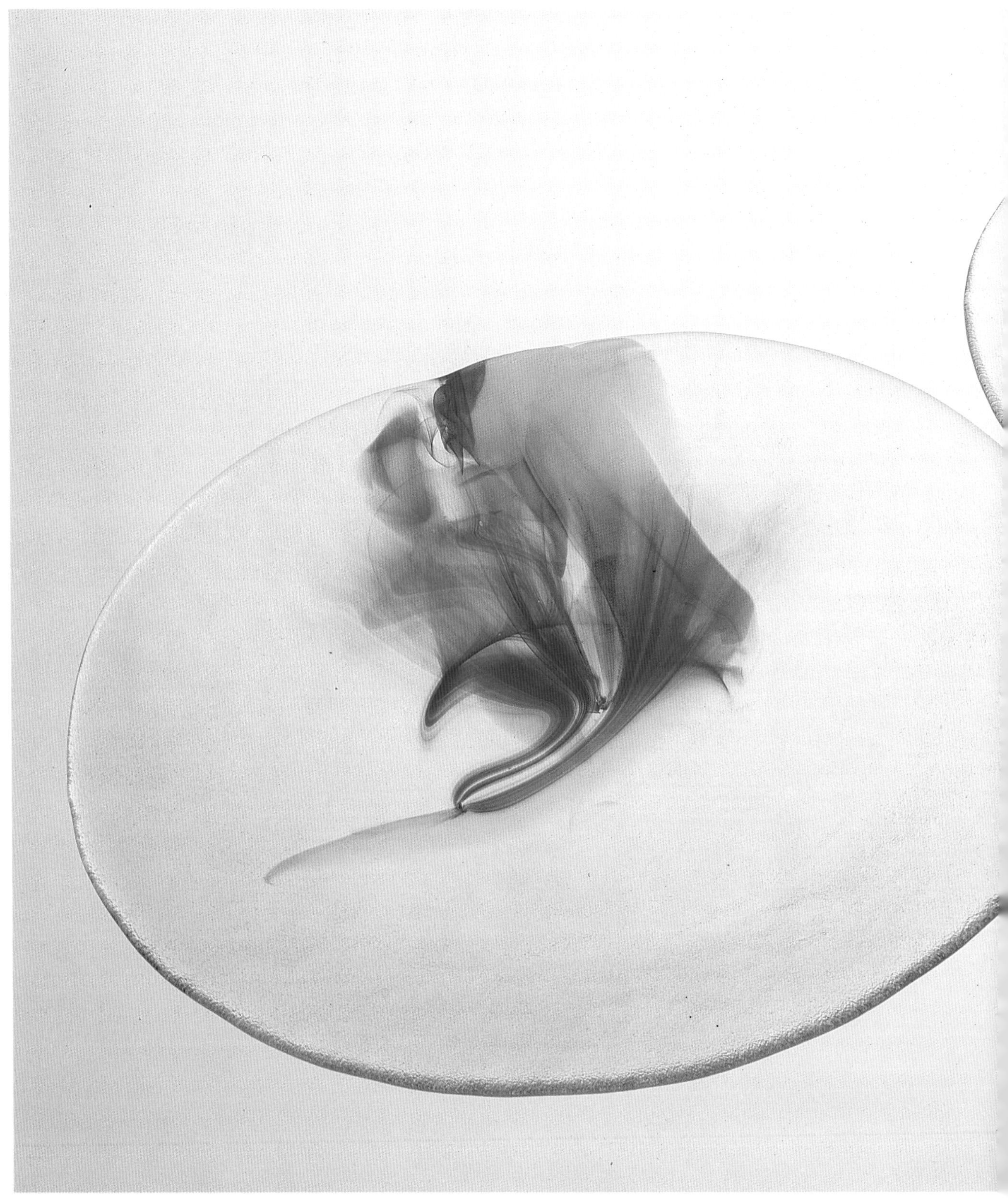

78540
Plate, 1/box
Fat, 1/kart
Ø: 16". 390 mm

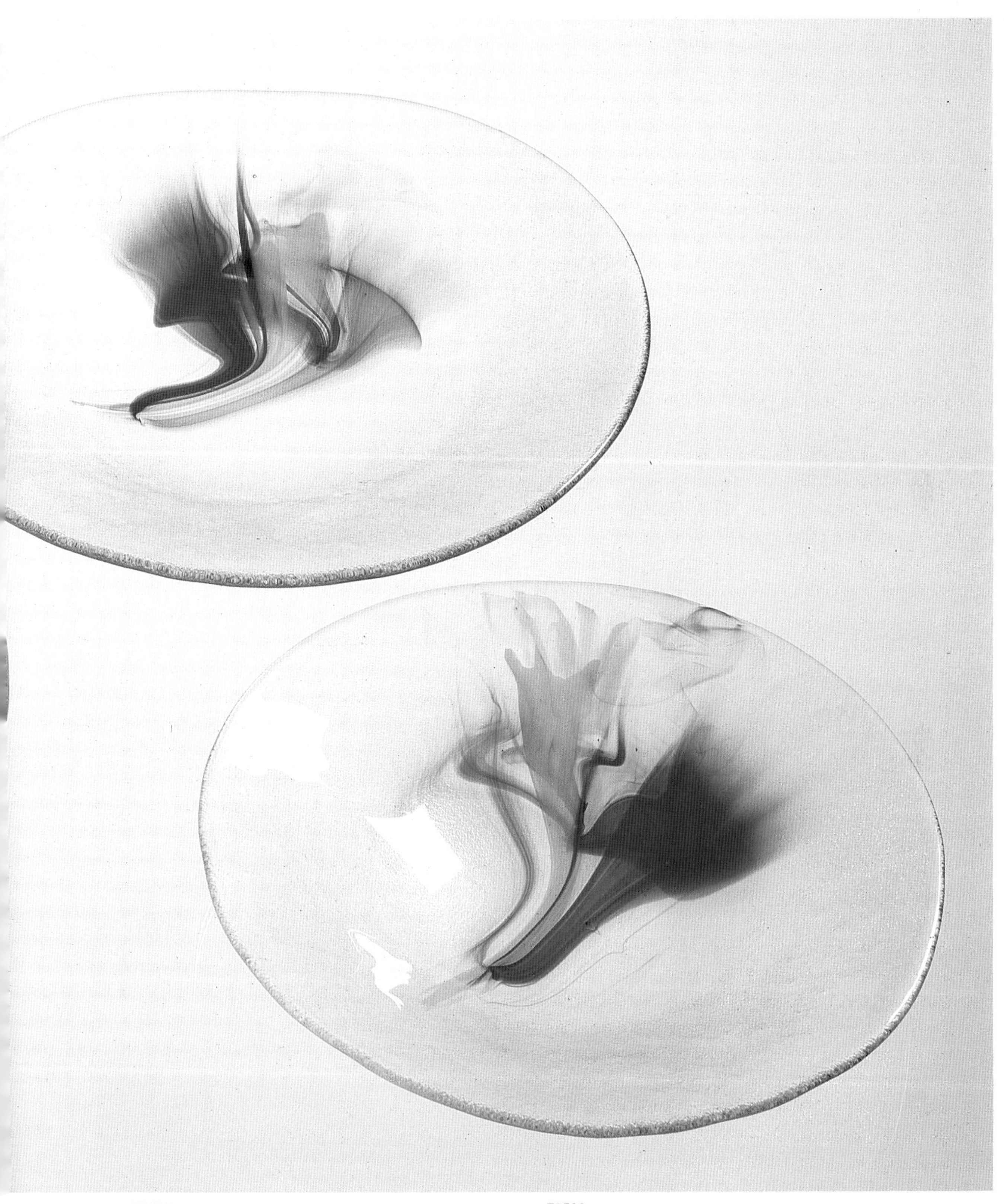

78539
PLATE, 1/BOX
FAT, 1/KART
Ø: 13″. 330 MM

78538
PLATE, 1/BOX
FAT, 1/KART
Ø: 10½″. 270 MM

TRUMPET

DESIGN: KJELL ENGMAN. HANDBLOWN. HANDBLÅST

68331	68330
CANDLESTICK	CANDLESTICK
LJUSSTAKE	LJUSSTAKE
H: 9½". 245 MM	H: 8". 200 MM

Tulip

Design: Bengt Edenfalk. Handblown, Full Lead Crystal. Handblåst, Kristall

48630	48628	48629
Vase	Vase	Vase
Vas	Vas	Vas
H: 8½". 215 mm	H: 8". 200 mm	H: 10½". 270 mm

Ulrica

Design: Bertil Vallien. Handblown. Handblåst

21104	21132	21108	21101	21125	21106
Wine, 4 oz, 2/box	Cognac, 10½ oz, 2/box	Wine, 11 oz, 2/box	Wine, 1 oz, 2/box	Aquavit, 2 oz, 2/box	Wine, 7 oz, 2/box
Vin, 10 cl, 2/kart	Cognac, 30 cl, 2/kart	Vin, 30 cl, 2/kart	Vin, 3 cl, 2/kart	Snaps, 5 cl, 2/kart	Vin, 20 cl, 2/kart
H: 6". 150 mm	H: 5½". 135 mm	H: 8¼". 210 mm	H: 5". 125 mm	H: 6". 150 mm	H: 7½". 190 mm
Ø: 2½". 65 mm	Ø: 2". 50 mm	Ø: 3½". 90 mm	Ø: 2". 50 mm	Ø: 2". 50 mm	Ø: 3". 75 mm

21103	21121	21131	21107	21122	21105
Wine, 3 oz, 2/box	Champagne flute, 6 oz, 2/box	Cognac, 5¼ oz, 2/box	Wine, 9 oz, 2/box	Champagne bowl, 6 oz, 2/box	Wine, 5¼ oz, 2/box
Vin, 7½ cl, 2/kart	Champagne hög, 17 cl, 2/kart	Cognac, 15 cl, 2/kart	Vin, 25 cl, 2/kart	Champagne skål, 17 cl, 2/kart	Vin, 15 cl, 2/kart
H: 5¾". 145 mm	H: 9½". 240 mm	H: 4¼". 115 mm	H: 8". 200 mm	H: 5¾". 145 mm	H: 7". 175 mm
Ø: 2¼". 60 mm	Ø: 1¾". 45 mm	Ø: 2". 50 mm	Ø: 3¼". 85 mm	Ø: 3¾". 95 mm	Ø: 2¾". 70 mm

Universe

Design: Bengt Edenfalk. Full Lead Crystal, Cut. Kristall, Slipad

58551
Bowl, Galax, 1/box
Skål, Galax, 1/kart
Ø: 6½". 170 mm

58453
Bowl, Venus, 1/box
Skål, Venus, 1/kart
Ø: 5½". 140 mm

Not shown:
Visas ej:

58451
Bowl,
Galax,
1/box
Skål,
Galax,
1/kart
Ø: 5½"
Ø: 140 mm

58452
Bowl,
Uranus,
1/box
Skål,
Uranus,
1/kart
Ø: 5½"
Ø: 140 mm

58553
Bowl,
Venus,
1/box
Skål,
Venus,
1/kart
Ø: 6½"
Ø: 170 mm

58552
Bowl, Uranus, 1/box
Skål, Uranus, 1/kart
Ø: 6½". 170 mm

Utopia

Design: Göran Wärff. Full Lead Crystal, Handblown, Cut. Kristall, Handblåst, Slipad

48020
Vase
Vas
H: 11". 280 mm

48018
Vase
Vas
H: 6½". 165 mm

48019
VASE
VAS
H: 8½". 220 MM

ULLA

DESIGN: KJELL ENGMAN

NOT SHOWN:
VISAS EJ:

58249
BOWL, 1/BOX
SKÅL, 1/KART
H: 4″
H: 105 MM
Ø: 6½″
Ø: 165 MM

58250
BOWL, 1/BOX. SKÅL, 1/KART
H: 5″. 130 MM. Ø: 8¼″. 210 MM

58248
DESSERT BOWL, 2/BOX. DESSERTSKÅL, 2/KART
Ø: 6¼″. 160 MM

78453
CAKE PLATE, 1 BOX. TÅRTFAT, 1/KART
Ø: 12½″. 320 MM

ULTIMA

DESIGN: ANNA EHRNER. FULL LEAD CRYSTAL. KRISTALL

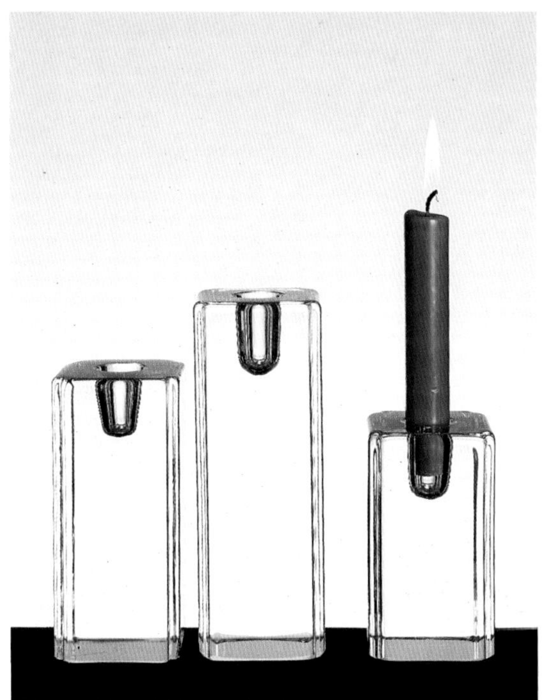

68306
CANDLESTICK
LJUSSTAKE
H: 5″. 130 MM

68307
CANDLESTICK
LJUSSTAKE
H: 6¼″. 160 MM

68305
CANDLESTICK
LJUSSTAKE
H: 4″. 100 MM

VALENTINE

DESIGN: BERTIL VALLIEN. HANDBLOWN. HANDBLÅST

48229
VASE, 1/BOX
VAS, 1/KART
H; 4″. 100 MM

You & Me

Design: Ulrica Hydman-Vallien. Handblown. Handblåst

Not shown:
Visas ej:

98517
Wine, 7 oz
2/box
Vin, 20 cl
2/kart
H: 9"
H: 230 mm

98519
Wine, 7 oz, lilac
Vin, 20 cl, lila
H: 9". 230 mm

98518
Wine, 7 oz, pink
Vin, 20 cl, rosa
H: 9". 230 mm

88517
Carafe, 35 oz, 1/box
Karaff, 100 cl, 1/kart
H: 9½". 240 mm

ZEBRA

DESIGN: BERTIL VALLIEN. HANDBLOWN. HANDBLÅST

48471
VASE, 1/BOX
VAS, 1/KART
H: 3". 75 MM

48474
VASE, 1/BOX
VAS, 1/KART
H: 6½". 170 MM

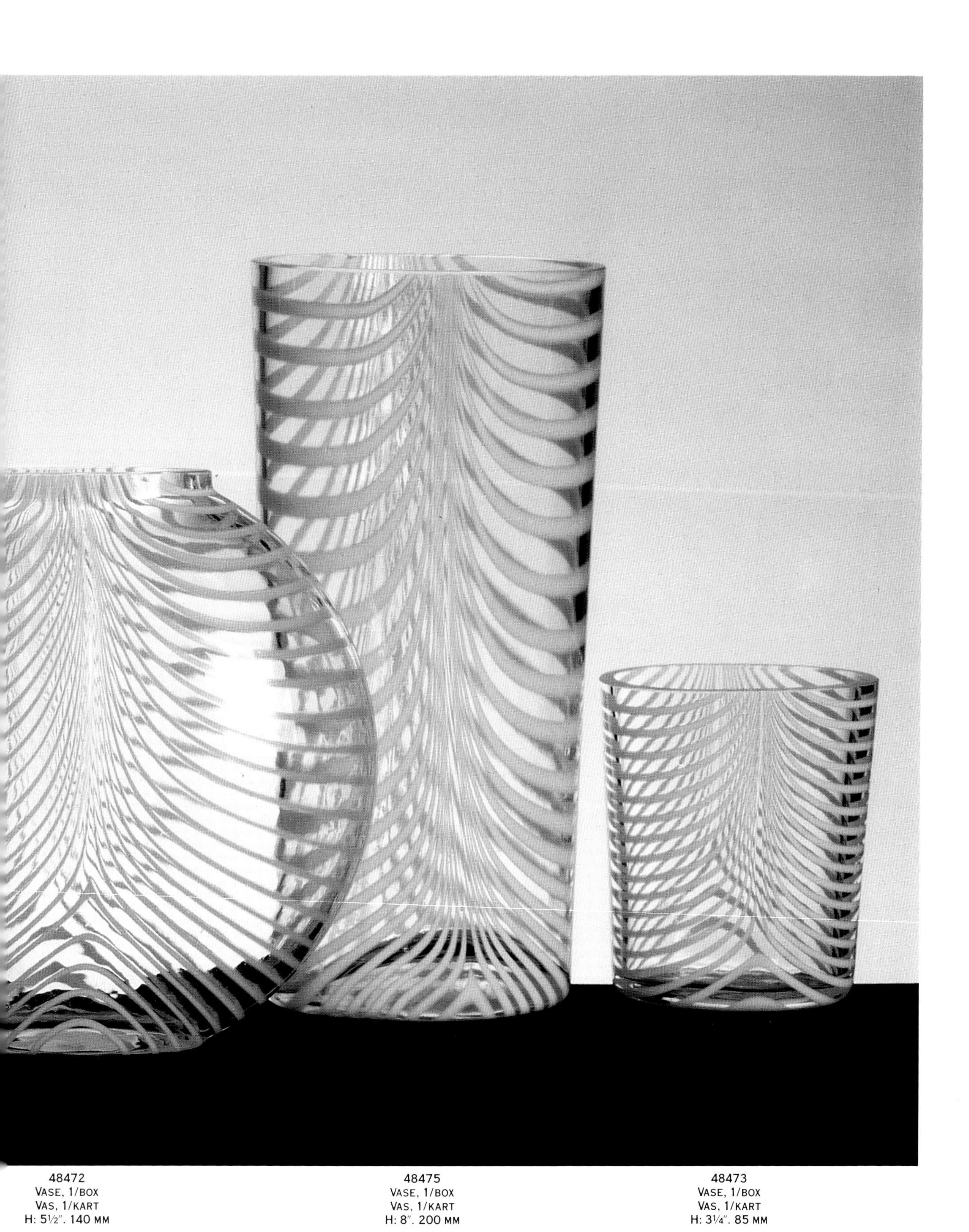

48472
VASE, 1/BOX
VAS, 1/KART
H: 5½". 140 MM

48475
VASE, 1/BOX
VAS, 1/KART
H: 8". 200 MM

48473
VASE, 1/BOX
VAS, 1/KART
H: 3¼". 85 MM

Zelda

Design: Monica Backström. Handblown. Handblåst

57596
Bowl, footed
Skål, på fot
H: 6¼". 160 mm
Ø: 7". 180 mm

67538
Hurricane, 1/box
Ljuslykta, 1/kart
H: 2¾". 70 mm
Ø: 4½". 115 mm

47539
Vase
Vas
H: 9½". 240 mm
Ø: 6". 150 mm

57595
Bowl, footed
Skål, på fot
H: 4". 100 mm
Ø: 5". 130 mm

57539
Bowl
Skål
H: 5½". 140 mm
Ø: 6½". 165 mm

67541
Hurricane, 1/box
Ljuslykta, 1/kart
H: 2". 50 mm
Ø: 3¼". 85 mm

47595
Vase
Vas
H: 6". 150 mm
Ø: 3". 75 mm

57538
Bowl
Skål
H: 4". 100 mm
Ø: 4¼". 110 mm

47538
Vase
Vas
H: 9½". 240 mm
Ø: 3". 75 mm

Zig-Zag

Design: Gun Lindblad. Handblown. Handblåst

Not shown:
Visas ej:

48343
Vase
Vas
H: 4¾"
H: 120 mm

48345
Vase
Vas
H: 8". 200 mm

48344
Vase
Vas
H: 6¼". 160 mm

Zoo

Design: Vicke Lindstrand. Full Lead Crystal. Kristall

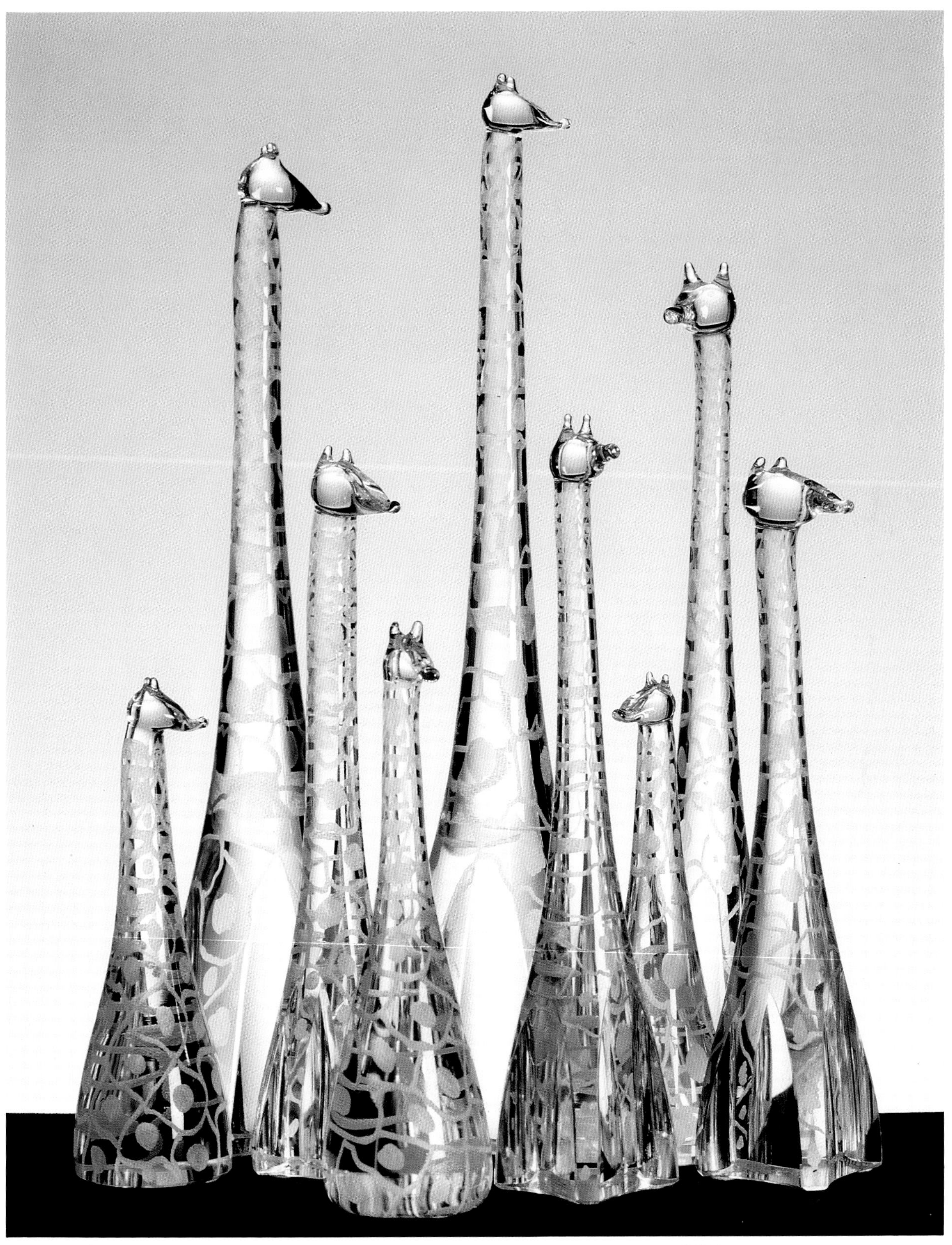

95729
Giraffe, engraved and cut
Giraff, graverad och slipad
H: 12¼". 310 mm

97183
Giraffe, engraved and cut
Giraff, graverad och slipad
H: 7". 180 mm

98044
Giraffe, engraved
Giraff, graverad
H: 5½". 140 mm

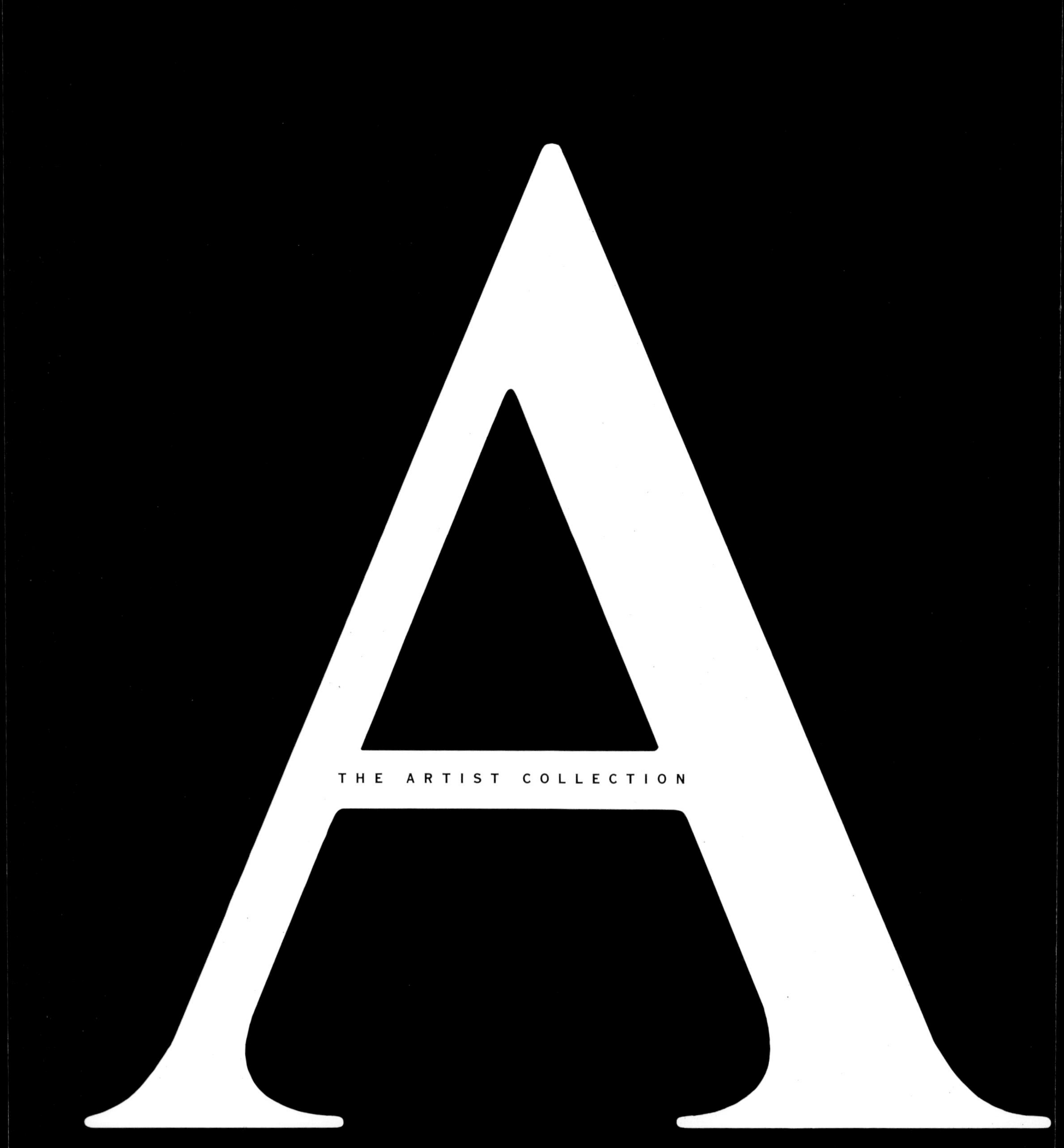
A
THE ARTIST COLLECTION

Artist Collection är lite mer spännande, mer avantgarde än resten av kollektionen. Detta är fantasiglas, skapat av Bertil Vallien och Ulrica Hydman-Vallien. De har hämtat inspiration från naturen, jorden, solen.
Resultatet är en kollektion som bara blir bättre med tiden.

Ces objets qui font partie de la collection principale sont un peu plus audacieux, plus avant-garde. C'est le verre fantaisie, créé par Bertil Vallien et Ulrica Hydman-Vallien. Il est tiré d'images de la nature, de textures du sol, de couleurs au coucher du soleil. C'est une collection qui ne peut que devenir plus belle avec le temps.

Part of the main collection, these pieces are a little more adventurous, more avantgarde. This is fantasy glass, created by Bertil Vallien and Ulrica Hydman-Vallien. It is spun from nature images, earth textures, sunset colors.
And it is a collection that can only improve with age.

Diese Stücke, die einen wichtigen Teil der Sammlung darstellen, sind etwas mehr abenteuerlich und avant-garde. Es ist Phantasieglas, kreiert von Bertil Vallien und Ulrica Hydman-Vallien. Geschaffen aus Naturdarstellungen, Erdstrukturen und Farben des Sonnenuntergangs.
Das Resultat ist eine Kollektion, die sich mit der Zeit verfeinert.

Antikva

Design: Bertil Vallien. Handblown. Handblåst

48009
Miniature bottle, 1/box
Miniatyrflaska, 1/kart
H: 3½". 85 mm

47866
Bottle
Flaska
H: 11". 280 mm

47836
Bottle
Flaska
H: 4". 100 mm

47834
Bottle
Flaska
H: 6½". 165 mm

48010
MINIATURE BOTTLE, 1/BOX
MINIATYRFLASKA, 1/KART
H: 4". 100 MM

48008
MINIATURE VASE, 1/BOX
MINIATYRVAS, 1/KART
H: 2". 50 MM

47865
BOTTLE
FLASKA
H: 10¼". 260 MM

58010
MINIATURE BOWL, 1/BOX
MINIATYRSKÅL, 1/KART
H: 1¾". 45 MM
Ø: 2". 50 MM

47835
BOTTLE
FLASKA
H: 6". 150 MM

APHRODITE

DESIGN: BERTIL VALLIEN. HANDBLOWN. HANDBLÅST

48532
VASE, PINK
VAS, ROSA
4½ × 5″. 110 × 125 MM

48535
VASE, BLACK/WHITE
VAS, SVART/VIT
7½ × 10″. 190 × 250 MM

48533
VASE, YELLOW
VAS, GUL
5 × 6¼″. 130 × 160 MM

48531	48530	48536	48534
VASE, GREEN, 1/BOX	VASE, BROWN, 1/BOX	VASE, BLACK/WHITE	VASE, WHITE
VAS, GRÖN, 1/KART	VAS, BRUN, 1/KART	VAS, SVART/VIT	VAS, VIT
2¼ × 2½". 60 × 65 MM	2¼ × 2½". 60 × 65 MM	10¼ × 6½". 260 × 170 MM	6 × 8". 150 × 200 MM

GALAXY BLUE

DESIGN: BERTIL VALLIEN. HANDBLOWN. HANDBLÅST

58015	68310	98014	58014	48015	48216
BOWL, ROUND, BLUE/YELLOW	OIL LAMP, 1/BOX	CUP	BOWL, ROUND	BOTTLE	MINIATURE VASE, 1/BOX
SKÅL, RUND, BLÅ/GUL	OLJELAMPA, 1/KART	POKAL	SKÅL, RUND	FLASKA	MINIATYRVAS, 1/KART
H: 5". 125 MM	H: 2¾". 70 MM	H: 8½". 220 MM	H: 3". 75 MM	H: 10¼". 260 MM	H: 4". 100 MM
Ø: 7". 180 MM		Ø: 5¾". 145 MM	Ø: 4¼". 110 MM		

48016
BOTTLE
FLASKA
H: 12¼". 310 MM

48014
BOTTLE
FLASKA
H: 8". 200 MM

48215
MINIATURE VASE, 1/BOX
MINIATYRVAS, 1/KART
H: 3". 75 MM

58214
MINIATURE BOWL, 1/BOX
MINIATYRSKÅL, 1/KART
Ø: 2¼". 60 MM

58016
BOWL, OVAL, BLUE/YELLOW
SKÅL, OVAL, BLÅ/GUL
H: 3¾". 95 MM
Ø: 5 × 4". 130 × 105 MM

48017
VASE
VAS
H: 6¼". 150 MM
Ø: 5¼ × 4¼". 135 × 110 MM

48214
MINIATURE VASE, 1/BOX
MINIATYRVAS, 1/KART
H: 2¾". 70 MM

GALAXY RED

DESIGN: BERTIL VALLIEN. HANDBLOWN. HANDBLÅST

48195	48199	48197	58195
BOTTLE	MINIATURE BOTTLE, 1/BOX	BOTTLE	BOWL, ROUND
FLASKA	MINIATYRFLASKA, 1/KART	FLASKA	SKÅL, RUND
H: 8". 200 MM	H: 3". 75 MM	H: 12¼". 310 MM	H: 3". 75 MM
			Ø: 4¼". 110 MM

58196	48196	48194	48198
Bowl, round	Bottle	Vase	Miniature vase, 1/box
Skål, rund	Flaska	Vas	Miniatyrvas, 1/kart
H: 5". 125 mm	H: 10¼". 260 mm	H: 6¼". 150 mm	H: 2¾". 70 mm
Ø: 7". 180 mm		Ø: 5¼ × 4¼". 135 × 110 mm	

Minos

Design: Bertil Vallien. Handblown. Handblåst

Miniature Bowl Miniatyrskål	Bowl Skål	Vase Vas	Vase Vas	Vase Vas
Ø: $2\frac{3}{4}$". 70 mm	Ø: $5\frac{3}{4}$". 145 mm	H: $6\frac{1}{2}$". 170 mm	H: $10\frac{1}{4}$". 260 mm	H: $4\frac{3}{4}$". 120 mm
58465 Blue. Blå	58436 Pink. Rosa	48438 Yellow. Gul	48439 Green. Grön	48466 Pink. Rosa
58435 Brown. Brun	58466 Brown. Brun	48468 Brown. Brun	48469 Pink. Rosa	48436 Blue. Blå

Miniature Vase Miniatyrvas H: 2″. 50 mm 48465 Yellow. Gul 48435 Brown. Brun	Vase Vas H: 5¾″. 145 mm 48437 Brown. Brun 48467 Green. Grön	Bowl Skål Ø: 4¾″. 120 mm 58464 White. Vit 58434 Blue. Blå	Bowl Skål Ø: 7″. 180 mm 58437 Blue. Blå 58467 Green. Grön	Bottle Flaska H: 3½″. 90 mm 48434 Black. Svart 48464 Yellow. Gul

Mythos

Design: Bertil Vallien, Ulrica Hydman-Vallien. Handblown. Handblåst

G	H	I	J	K	L
98569	98555	98572	98559	98571	98558
Heracles Paperweight	Amos Paperweight	Hermes Paperweight	Ariadne Paperweight	Icarus Paperweight	Myrrha Paperweight
Heracles Brevpress	Amos Brevpress	Hermes Brevpress	Ariadne Brevpress	Icarus Brevpress	Myrrha Brevpress
H: 3¼". 85 mm	H: 2". 55 mm	H: 1¾". 45 mm	H: 1". 30 mm	H: 2". 55 mm	H: 1½". 40 mm
Ø: 3". 75 mm	Ø: 2". 55 mm	Ø: 3". 75 mm	Ø: 2". 55 mm	Ø: 3". 75 mm	Ø: 2". 55 mm

A	B	C	D	E	F
98570	98573	98563	98561	98557	98562
Midas Paperweight	Achilles Paperweight	Hera Paperweight	Eurydike Paperweight	Lysistrate Paperweight	Medea Paperweight
Midas Brevpress	Achilles Brevpress	Hera Brevpress	Eurydike Brevpress	Lysistrate Brevpress	Medea Brevpress
H: 1½". 40 mm	H: 2". 50 mm	H: 1½". 40 mm	H: 1½". 40 mm	H: 2". 55 mm	H: 1½". 40 mm
Ø: 3". 75 mm	Ø: 3". 75 mm	Ø: 2". 55 mm	Ø: 2". 55 mm	Ø: 2". 55 mm	Ø: 2". 55 mm

M	N	O	P	Q	R
98567	98556	98565	98566	98560	98568
Apollo Paperweight	Daphne Paperweight	Orpheus Paperweight	Poseidon Paperweight	Athene Paperweight	Helios Paperweight
Apollo Brevpress	Daphne Brevpress	Orpheus Brevpress	Poseidon Brevpress	Athene Brevpress	Helios Brevpress
H: 3". 75 mm	H: 2". 55 mm	H: 2¾". 70 mm	H: 1½". 40 mm	H: 1½". 40 mm	H: 1½". 40 mm
Ø: 3". 75 mm	ø: 2". 55 mm	Ø: 3". 75 mm	Ø: 3". 75 mm	Ø: 2". 55 mm	Ø: 3". 75 mm

NETWORK

DESIGN: BERTIL VALLIEN. HANDBLOWN. HANDBLÅST

58012
MINIATURE BOWL, 1/BOX
MINIATYRSKÅL, 1/KART
H: 2". 55 MM
Ø: 2¾". 70 MM

47864
BOTTLE
FLASKA
H: 9½". 240 MM

57862
BOWL
SKÅL
Ø: 4". 100 MM

47863
BOTTLE
FLASKA
H: 8". 200 MM

48012
MINIATURE VASE/BOTTLE, 1/BOX
MINIATYRVAS/FLASKA, 1/KART
H: 4". 105 MM

47862
BOTTLE
FLASKA
H: 6". 150 MM

48011
MINIATURE VASE, 1/BOX
MINIATYRVAS, 1/KART
H: 3". 75 MM

47967
VASE WITH BLUE DOT
VAS MED BLÅ PUNKT
H: 6". 150 MM

Paradise

Design: Ulrica Hydman-Vallien. Handblown, Handpainted. Handblåst, Handmålad

58516	48515	98516	98515
Bowl	Vase	Cup	Cup
Skål	Vas	Pokal	Pokal
Ø: 4½". 115 mm	H: 3½". 90 mm	H: 10". 250 mm	H: 6½". 170 mm

58517	58515	48517	48516
Bowl	Bowl	Vase	Vase
Skål	Skål	Vas	Vas
Ø: 7¼". 185 mm	Ø: 2¾". 70 mm	H: 8¼". 210 mm	H: 6". 150 mm

Tornado

Design: Bertil Vallien. Handblown. Handblåst

58279	58280	48281	48286
Bowl	Bowl	Bottle	Miniature bottle, 1/box
Skål	Skål	Flaska	Miniatyrflaska, 1/kart
H: 4". 100 mm	H: 5". 125 mm	H: 9½". 240 mm	H: 3¼". 85 mm
Ø: 4½". 115 mm	Ø: 6". 150 mm		

48279
BOTTLE
FLASKA
H: 4¼". 110 MM

48280
BOTTLE
FLASKA
H: 7". 175 MM

48285
MINIATURE BOTTLE, 1/BOX
MINIATYRFLASKA, 1/KART
H: 2½". 65 MM

48278
MINIATURE VASE, 1/BOX
MINIATYRVAS, 1/KART
H: 2". 50 MM

Volcano

Design: Bertil Vallien. Handblown. Handblåst

48138
Vase
Vas
H: 8". 200 mm

58136
Bowl
Skål
H: 3¼". 85 mm
Ø: 4¾". 120 mm

58137
Bowl
Skål
H: 5". 130 mm
Ø: 6½". 170 mm

Volcano

Design: Bertil Vallien. Handblown. Handblåst

48136	48139	48137	68311
Vase	Miniature vase, 1/box	Vase	Oil lamp, 1/box
Vas	Miniatyrvas, 1/kart	Vas	Oljelampa, 1/kart
H: 4¼". 110 mm	H: 2¼". 60 mm	H: 6¼". 160 mm	H: 2¾". 70 mm

Pastel

Design: Ulrica Hydman-Vallien. Handblown. Handblåst

78013	88013	58013	48013
Miniature dish, 1/box	Miniature jug, 1/box	Miniature bowl, 1/box	Miniature vase, 1/box
Miniatyrfat, 1/kart	Miniatyrkanna, 1/kart	Miniatyrskål, 1/kart	Miniatyrvas, 1/kart
Ø: 3½". 90 mm	H: 2". 55 mm	H: 2". 55 mm Ø: 2½". 65 mm	H: 2". 55 mm

Wind Pipes

Design: Bertil Vallien. Handblown. Handblåst

48174	48173	48177	48176	48175
Vase	Vase	Vase	Vase	Vase
Vas	Vas	Vas	Vas	Vas
H: 9½". 240 mm	H: 7". 180 mm	H: 15". 390 mm	H: 8". 200 mm	H: 13". 330 mm

Addresses.

HEAD OFFICE:
KOSTA BODA AB
S-360 52 KOSTA
SWEDEN
TEL+46 478 503 00
FAX+46 478 502 20
TLX 52014 KOSTABO S

SWEDEN:
KOSTA BODA AB
BOX 7567
S-103 93 STOCKHOLM 7
SWEDEN
TEL+46-8 20 37 44

KOSTA BODA AB
ÖSTRA HAMNGATAN 52
S-411 09 GÖTEBORG
SWEDEN
TEL+46-31 13 81 35

KOSTA BODA AB
SKOMAKAREGATAN 2
S-211 34 MALMÖ
SWEDEN
TEL+46-40 97 05 05

The Representatives:

ARGENTINA:
STEINTHAL SAIC
ARENGREEN 1039/41
BUENOS AIRES
ARGENTINA
TEL+54-190 2726
TLX 33-21065 AR TRI
MESSAGE FOR GOLDSCHMIDT

AUSTRALIA:
KOSTA BODA AUSTRALIA PTY LTD
P O BOX 362
ARTARMON NSW 2064
AUSTRALIA
TEL+61-242 826 55
FAX+61-24 274 636
TLX 071-24374 KOSTA AA
CABLE BODAGLASS SYDNEY

BELGIUM, LUXEMBOURG
STENVER-ENGEL S.A.
AVENUE LOUIS LEPOUTRE, 97
B-1060 BRUXELLES
BELGIUM
TEL+32-234 474 04
TLX 46-25525 TRADIX B

CANADA:
SAMACO TRADING LTD
55 E EASTBEAVER CREEK ROAD
RICHMOND HILL, ONTARIO
L4B 1E8
CANADA
TEL+1-416 731 32 32
TLX 21-06 964 533 SAMACOTRAY TOR
FAX+1-4167 310 872
CABLE SAMACOTRAY, TORONTO

CYPRUS:
SCAN-SELLER
ARCH MAKARIOS 111 AVE 27 B
118 NICOSIA
CYPRUS

DENMARK:
GENSE A/S
MAGLEBJERGVEJ 17
DK-2800 KGS LYNGBY
DENMARK
TEL+45-288 25 44
TLX 55-37738 GENSE DK

FRANCE:
KOSTA BODA FRANCE SARL
Z.I. DE COURTABOEUF
BATIMENT EVOLIC NO 8
AVENUE DU QUEBEC
F-91940 LES ULIS
FRANCE
TEL+33-164 462 021
TLX 42-690 109

GREAT BRITAIN:
DEXAM INTERNATIONAL LTD
HASLEMERE
SURREY
GREAT BRITAIN
TEL+44-428 41 72
TLX 51-858 397 DEXAM G

GREECE:
STUDIO KOSTA BODA
40 B-IOAKIM
KALANAKI, ATEN
GREECE

ICELAND:
MAR EGILSSON H.F.
BLIKANES 28
GARDABAER
ISLAND
TEL+354-113 122
TLX 0501-2223 FRON IS

ITALY:
MICHELINI RAPPRESENTANZE
VIA CHIASSO 11
I-201 55 MILANO
ITALY
TEL+39-232 711 44
TLX 43-325 014 MIRAMI

JAPAN:
SEIBU DEPARTMENT STORES LTD
50TH FLOOR SUNSHINE 60
1-1, 3-CHOME
HIGASHI IKEBUKURO
TOSHIMA-KU
TOKYO
JAPAN
TEL+81-398 901 11
TLX 72-22506 SEIBU J
CABLE SEIBUDEPT TOKYO

THE NETHERLANDS:
BERTRAMS B.V
PENNINGWEG 29
NL-4879 AE ETTEN-LEUR
THE NETHERLANDS
TEL+31-1608 209 48
TEL: SHOWROOM 309 448 01
TLX 44-74184 CEBIM NL

NEW ZEALAND:
PACIFIC IMPORT CO LTD
P O BOX 9489
56 TORY STREET
WELLINGTON 1
NEW ZEALAND
TEL+64-857 609
TLX PREPAC NZ 74-306 79

NORWAY:
KOSTA BODA NORGE
NIELS JUELSGATE 24
N-0205 OSLO 2
TEL+47-239 18 11

SPAIN:
RIERA
VILAMARI, 72
08015 BARCELONA 15
SPAIN
TEL+34-332 574 93, 584 78
TLX 52-50114 RIRA E

SWITZERLAND:
KOSTA BODA SUISSE SA
MARKGRÄFLERSTRASSE 84
CH-4021 BASEL
SWITZERLAND
TEL+41-613 219 13
TLX 45-963 898 BODA CH
FAX+41-61 32 62 03

USA:
KOSTA BODA USA LTD
4 SPERRY ROAD
FAIRFIELD, NJ 07006
USA
TEL+1-201 575 5579
FAX+1-201 575 6280
TLX 23-666 309 KOSTA UW
SHOWROOM: TEL+1-212 679 2280

VENEZUELA:
G.A.L. COMPANIA ANONIMA
P O BOX
APARTADO 329
CARACAS 1010-A
VENEZUELA
TEL+58-254 136 11
TLX 31-28448 GALCA VC
CABLE GAL-CARACAS

WEST GERMANY, AUSTRIA:
FIRMA MERCANTILE—F LINDENAU
ROBERT-KOCH-STR 4
D-8033 PLANEGG/MÜNCHEN
WEST GERMANY
TEL+49-898 596 935
TLX 41-52 12 387 MERC D
CABLE LINDIMEX MÜNCHEN

HONG KONG, TAIWAN, REPUBLIC OF CHINA, PEOPLE'S REPUBLIC OF CHINA:
INSPIRATION AB
BIRGER JARLSG 97
S-113 56 STOCKHOLM
SWEDEN
TLX 10788 HEURLEN S
TEL+46-8 15 58 82

EGYPT, KUWAIT, LIBYA, IRAK, QUATAR, BAHRAIN, UNITED ARAB EMIRATES, OMAN, NORTH YEMEN, SUDAN, PAKISTAN, JORDANIA, SYRIA, SRI LANKA:
MERX LTD
P O BOX 21
S-401 20 GÖTEBORG
SWEDEN
STREET ADDRESS:
KRONHUSGATAN 16
S-401 20 GÖTEBORG
SWEDEN
TEL+46-31 131 000/7
TLX 21900 SWEDTRADE S